The Windows to His World

Trevor Kincaid at age 55.

The Windows to His World

The Story of Trevor Kincaid

Muriel L. Guberlet

Pacific Books, Publishers   Palo Alto, California

921
K51g
c.2

International Standard Book Number 0-87015-210-6.
Library of Congress Catalog Card Number 73-91594.
Printed and bound in the United States of America.

PACIFIC BOOKS, PUBLISHERS
P. O. Box 558, Palo Alto, California 94302

Foreword

TREVOR KINCAID WAS born in Peterborough, Ontario, in 1872. Removing with his family to Olympia, Washington in 1889, he quickly built himself a reputation as an insect collector. By the time he entered the University of Washington in 1894, he had sent 100,000 specimens to various entomologists in the eastern United States, and as a result was invited on collecting expeditions to the Pribilof Islands in 1897 and to southern Alaska in 1898. L. O. Howard of the United States Department of Agriculture employed him in 1908 and 1909 to collect parasites of the gypsy moth in Japan and Russia. Meanwhile, he had become professor of zoology at the University of Washington and was laying foundations for what was to become a leading center of biological study in the northwestern United States.

This is, in essence, the story Muriel Guberlet is telling in this book. The widow of John E. Guberlet, who from 1923 to 1940 was a member of Kincaid's department, Mrs. Guberlet is well qualified to explore in depth Trevor Kincaid's life.

From long personal acquaintance with Professor Kincaid, I am able to testify to the faithfulness of Mrs. Guberlet's narrative. For nearly twenty years after I became a member of the Department of Zoology of the University of Washington in 1927, I was in almost

42959

daily contact with Trevor Kincaid. I had not been in
Seattle a week before he began to take me on insect-
collecting trips. He and I both lived in the same direction from the campus, and I used to walk part way
to lunch with him regularly. I rate my contacts with
Trevor Kincaid as having influenced my professional
life as much as any I had with my undergraduate and
graduate professors.

This book about Professor Kincaid is commended
to those who knew him personally as well as those
interested in the cultural history of Seattle and the
Pacific Northwest.

MELVILLE H. HATCH
Professor of Zoology
University of Washington

Acknowledgments

WHEN I BEGAN writing a biography of Trevor Kincaid, many of his old-time friends wrote or telephoned me recounting recollections of him or humorous stories attributed to him. My regret is that, because of lack of space, I could not record as many of these as I wished. But they all added to my understanding of him as a scientist, an environmentalist, and as a man.

I gleaned much information, especially about his early life in Peterborough, Ontario, from his autobiography. I visited with him often. I heard of his activities in Olympia at the time Washington became a state, of his wanderings through the woods to collect insects, of his early student days at the University, of his becoming a bottle washer there at $25.00 a month, of his experiences as an investigator of baffling biological problems in far places, of his founding of the Marine Station at Friday Harbor, and of his work with the oyster industry in Washington. Trevor Kincaid had a prodigious memory, recalling the minutest details of events long past.

Trevor Kincaid's daughters told of the love their father gave them as babies and small children and of his later attempts to interest them in biology.

There are hundreds of items about him in the Seattle newspapers, in the University Dailies, in the

Northwest collection in the University of Washington library, and miscellaneous sources. Of course his published works and his research papers are on file in the University library. All of these I referred to often.

Dr. Melville H. Hatch, a fellow entomologist and for many years a colleague of Kincaid, gave me continuous help and encouragement. His hope was that I write a definitive biography of the professor, while I wished to present him as a splendid scientist, a dedicated teacher, a lover of nature, and a delightful human being.

Contents

List of Illustrations

The Windows to His World

CHAPTER 1

Why Does the Moon Run Away?

THE COURSE OF Trevor Kincaid's life was undoubtedly determined by his compelling desire to "know," not only to "know" but to know "why." When he was three years of age, he demanded that his mother tell him why the moon changed. At 97 he was still asking "why." Why are the oysters in Willapa Bay smaller now than they were twenty-five years ago, and what ecological factors have caused the change? He had to know.

From earliest childhood he had an insatiable curiosity about the world around him. Everything in nature delighted him—the moon, stars, flowers, rocks, butterflies, birds, spiders. Almost from the time he could walk, he collected, preserved, and recorded facts about living things. When just a boy, he said, "I would rather watch a spider spin its web than shake hands with the President." Willing to go anywhere or do anything in the interest of science, he was filled with equal wonder at man's conquest of the moon and at the discovery of a new beetle or an unfamilar insect.

As a result of his study of the insignificant creatures of the earth, Trevor Kincaid became one of the world's best-known entomologists. He wrote twenty-five scientific papers and had seventy-two species of animals named in his honor. In 1969 a new research building on the University campus was named Trevor Kincaid Hall.

Trevor's curiosity, his wish to know, first became evident in 1875, when he refused to go to bed because he wanted to see where the moon went. Almost every evening, he sat on the porch of his home in Peterborough, Ontario, and questioned his mother about the ever-changing moon.

"It's nine o'clock, time you were fast asleep," she answered.

"I won't go to bed. I have to see where it goes."

"You can look at the moon tomorrow night, and the next and the next. It isn't going to run away," his mother assured him.

"But it does run away. A few weeks ago it was thin as a thread. Soon it was like a big round ball. Then I didn't see it for a while. Now it's thin again, and it isn't in the same place. I have to know where it goes and what makes it change," the small, intense boy rattled on.

"I'm afraid I can't explain the changes of the moon very well," she sighed. "It has something to do with the rotation of the earth around the sun. I'll have your father explain it to you." After a dozen more questions, she got her son in bed. As she turned off the new-fangled gaslight and closed the door, she brushed her hand across her brow and thought, "Well, he can't ask any more questions before morning." Already she was realizing that her youngest son was extremely precocious.

Trevor Kincaid was fortunate in having parents who could answer many of his questions. His father was a young physician in Peterborough. His mother had been educated in music, art, and literature in

Montreal, but when he began inquiring about the moon and its path across the skies, she knew she could not answer his queries either to her own satisfaction or to his. She knew her husband would be able to give him satisfactory answers, but he was rarely at home when the matter of the moon presented itself, for almost every evening he had to drive to the country to set a broken leg, deliver a baby, or ease pains in someone's stomach.

The first evening the doctor was at home, however, he did his best to explain the phases of the moon to the eager child and convinced him that one had to have a telescope to watch the heavens. He promised that the next time he went to Toronto, where there was a telescope, Trevor could go with him. With this assurance, the small boy turned his attention to matters nearer at hand.

Moths and butterflies that flew across the porch next intrigued the child. He hunted insects and aphids on the lilac and rose bushes in the back yard, where he found more than a hundred minute forms of life. When the back yard was exhausted as a collecting ground, he and his brothers, Morden and Kenneth, explored the right-of-way along the railroad tracks, the river, and the hills. Although Trevor was much younger than his brothers, his eyes were far sharper than theirs in finding living things. When their father scolded them for wandering so far from home, Trevor answered, "You told us the name Kincaid meant 'wooded hills.' If that is true, we should know about them, shouldn't we?"

Peterborough in the 1870's was a thriving farming community of about six or seven thousand persons, mostly of Scotch and Irish descent, on the Otonobee River, which rises in the picturesque group of glacial lakes to the north and flows southward into Lake Ontario.

Dr. Kincaid had lived in Peterborough most of his life. His father had died of typhoid fever in Donegal during the famine and pestilence in Ireland in the middle of the nineteenth century, and his mother, hoping for a better life for her children than she could provide in Ireland, brought them to Canada to be near her husband's relatives.

At eighteen, Robert, her youngest son, was apprenticed to Dr. George Burnham, a local physician. The young man, who was industrious and likable, accompanied the doctor on his calls, recorded the patient's symptoms, and held the doctor's scissors, forceps, and scalpel during operations. He also wrote down the prescriptions, made up the medicines, and delivered them to the patients.

After a two-year apprenticeship, Robert enrolled as a medical student in Queen's University in Kingston, Ontario. During the summer vacations, to help pay his expenses in medical school, he served as a purser on a boat plying the St. Lawrence River between Montreal and Quebec, making friends with the townspeople along the way. Among them was a beautiful girl named Mary Margaret Bell, with whom Robert fell deeply in love. When summer was over and it was time for him to return to school, he gave his sweetheart a kiss and solemnly swore he would not forget her.

Robert received his medical degree in 1863 and went to New York to serve his internship in Bellevue Hospital. While in New York, he was caught up in the excitement of the American Civil War, and left Bellevue to volunteer in the medical corps of the Union Army. His first assignment was with a field service unit following the troops from place to place, from battleground to battleground. He was never to forget the sickness and suffering of the soldiers in these field hospitals, the crude instruments used in operations, the incredible number of amputations, the terrific death rates, the mass burials. Antiseptic surgery was still in the future, and operations were terrible ordeals.

After this grueling baptism into medical practice, Robert Kincaid served on the staff of the Armory Square Hospital in Washington, D.C., where fortunately there was a semblance of professional medical practice for the hundreds of men who were crowded into every corner of the hospital. At the close of hostilities in 1865, he was sent to Maine to help muster out the soldiers returning to their homes.

As a result of these harrowing experiences, the young doctor was not at all sure he wanted to practice medicine. But by this time Dr. Burnham was eager to retire and, having great faith in his erstwhile assistant, he persuaded Robert to take over his practice.

With the older doctor's practice almost thrust upon him, Dr. Kincaid settled down in Peterborough and married Mary Margaret Bell, his sweetheart of steamboat days.

A case that undoubtedly enhanced his reputation as a promising surgeon was that of a young man who, while working in the harvest fields, slipped and fell into the machinery of the thresher and suffered a serious skull injury. The more experienced doctors shook their heads and refused to treat the injured man. As a last resort, Dr. Kincaid was called. He was not sure he could save the boy, but he wasn't going to stand by and let him die for want of trying. Using a trephine, a small circular saw, he removed a piece of shattered bone from his head and inserted in its place a silver plate, a new and daring operation in the 1860's. The older doctors prophesied the worst.

The young man's family moved to Manitoba, and Dr. Kincaid lost touch with him. However, one evening several years later, the doctor was sitting in his living room when a large bearded man was ushered in. The visitor walked directly to the doctor and asked, "Do you recognize me?" Without waiting for an answer, he pulled off his cap and exhibited the silver plate in his skull.

As the town grew and prospered, Dr. Kincaid's practice also prospered, and his family grew apace. Soon he had three extremely active sons and a daughter. In order to give direction to the boys' ramblings and to encourage their love of the out-of-doors, he bought a large farm a couple of miles outside of town. At first, all the children had great fun on the farm. After a few months, however, the older boys tired of looking at birds, chasing rabbits, and fishing, but the farm became Trevor's world. He peered under rocks and examined the bark of trees for insects. Soon he was carrying an insect net as he walked back and forth to the farm. He roamed through the woods and drifted in a rowboat on the stream that ran across the farm. On summer afternoons he lay on its bank, looked at the clouds, and dreamed.

When he discovered that the creek was swarming with tiny animals and plants, Trevor begged his father for vials into which to put his findings; he strained the water for polliwogs; discovered the stages of a butterfly's development; collected insects; and planted a garden. Very methodically, he dug trenches in which to plant peas. He set out tomato plants, hilled up cucumber vines, and strung up beans. To Trevor's great disappointment, the apple orchard his father planted was not very successful, because he bought scrubby trees from an itinerant peddler and the apples turned out to be shriveled, sour russets.

By this time, Dr. Kincaid was so busy attending to his large practice that he had little time for his family. Mrs. Kincaid, with the help of a cook, nursemaid, and stable boy, provided a happy, well-regulated family life. Dr. Kincaid, a man of decidedly strong convictions, did not send his children to school until they were eight years old, believing there were many ways to learn outside of the schoolroom. Much of the children's early training, therefore, fell to Mrs. Kincaid, a highly intelligent woman. During the long winter months, with her children gathered around the big stove in the parlor, amid a feeling of serenity and security, she read the few children's books available. Then she turned to the novels of Scott and Dickens. Of course, most of these stories were above Trevor's head, but the rhythm of his mother's voice soothed the child and lulled him to sleep. Soon he was pleading, "I want to read too. If you can read, why can't I?"

"You're too young to read."

"No, I'm not. You always try to tell me I'm too young. I can do lots more things than you think I can."

Thus it came about that while almost an infant, Trevor began to fill his mind with the words of the printed page. He read every book he could get his hands on, but his favorite was *Peter the Whaler.* Soon he could repeat it by heart. Then he read about the

Napoleonic Wars. He learned the names of all the
kings of England—Alfred the Great; Edward the Elder; Athelstan; Edmund the Elder; Edred the Fair;
Edgar the Peaceful, etc., down to modern times. His
remarkable memory allowed him to store away all
manner of facts for future use. By the time he went
to school, he had become a voracious reader. He had
devoured all the books in his home and turned to his
father's tomes, the works of Tyndall, Huxley, and
Darwin.

During the winter of his seventh year, Trevor was
dumped into a pool of icy water while bobsledding.
The ducking resulted in an attack of pleurisy, which
kept him in bed for several weeks. When he could
not bear to stay indoors another minute, without telling his mother, he put on his warmest coat and cap
and ran to a nearby greenhouse. In a very business-
like manner he approached the owner and asked for
a job. The proprietor laughed and said, "A boy your
age doesn't know the difference between a weed and
the rarest flower, or a carnation from a sweet pea."

"Sure I do. We have a book at home about flowers.
I've looked at it so many times I can recognize most
of them and can say their scientific names. A carnation is a *Dianthus* and a sweet pea is a *Laturus adora-
tus.*"

Within a week Trevor was watering the plants in
the greenhouse, fertilizing them, transplanting the
choicest varieties, and learning more and more scientific names. All his life the boy remembered the
wonderful sensation of stepping out of the snow and
ice of the bitter Canadian winter into the greenhouse
with its warmth and fragrance. But the best part of
the job was making friends with Harry, the caretaker, an elderly mulatto, and his wife, the only col-

Trevor at 5 in a Scottish kilt.

Dr. Robert Kincaid and his family. Standing, Doctor Kincaid and Morden. Seated (left to right), Trevor, Zoe, Mrs. Kincaid, and Kenneth.

ored people in Peterborough. Harry's most treasured
possessions were a number of mystery novels. When
the plants were all watered and tended, Trevor
loved to curl up in a comfortable chair in Harry's tiny
sitting room and read the blood-curdling stories of an
earlier day.

In time he came to know every inch of the farm,
but he loved it as much as ever. Now he added another dimension to his observations of the out-of-
doors. As he walked to and from the farm, he noticed
that the countryside was littered with boulders,
which his father told him had been brought down
from the north by glaciers during the Ice Age. The
farmers around Peterborough, no doubt believing
with Robert Frost that "good fences make good
neighbors," had separated their fields with strong
rock walls.

In cutting the boulders, the quarry men had left
great piles of discarded materials along the road-
ways. Hidden deep in many of the boulders were
shining quartz, mica, and garnet. Now, in addition to
his insect net, Trevor carried a cold chisel and a
hatchet on his rambles. Often he found so many precious stones that he would drag home a sackful of
shining "gems" after a day's work.

Even more exciting than finding minerals was discovering fossils hidden deep in the boulders. How
had these beautiful shells and leaves become embed-
ded in the rocks? He had to find out.

Then he remembered that in the tall bookcase in
the parlor was a set of books called *Reports of the
Canadian Geological Survey.* Maybe they would tell
him about fossils. Dragging a chair to the bookcase to
stand on, he lifted down one of the heavy volumes.
On the cover of the book were the words "Compiled

by Robert Bell." Why, Robert Bell was his cousin. Soon the pages of the *Reports* were dog-eared and soiled from constant thumbing, and the small boy with the inquiring mind could identify dozens of fossils. There were so many things to do and think about around Peterborough.

But certainly it was the gift of a microscope, when Trevor was seven years old, that opened one of the widest windows of his life. On looking into that miraculous device for the first time, young Trevor was beside himself with wonder that a tiny glass could make the wing of a butterfly as beautiful as lace or magnify a grain of pollen a hundred times. And the wonder of that microscope never left him.

In the ninety years after he received that exciting gift, it is safe to say that scarcely a day passed that he did not peer through the eyepiece of a microscope, and the work of much of his life revolved around it.

During the summer of 1879 he went with his mother to Bellsville, Ontario, to visit her sister, Mrs. Potts. His cousin, James Potts, who was about ten years older than Trevor, became the boy's idol by introducing him to hitherto undreamt-of scientific wonders. James, a medical student at McGill University, had recently bought a new microscope and gave his old one to the young visitor.

For days the enchanted little boy sat before the magic microscope peering at insects, grains of sand, leaves, pieces of fabric—everything. Hearing of Trevor's fascination with the newfound wonder, an elderly German who lived close to the Potts's, showed him how to study diatoms, plants so small that a teaspoon can hold a million individuals no larger than a pinprick. As Trevor looked at diatoms through the magic lens, each tiny speck was like a crystal box, the top and bottom fitting together so perfectly that when the strands of protoplasm and amber pigment caught the light, they looked like a basket filled with jewels.

James Potts also taught his cousin to mount moths, butterflies, and other insects like a professional entomologist, each one labeled with the common and scientific name, and the date and place of collection. James and his mother had spent several summers on the Atlantic seaboard, where he had gathered clams, snails, starfish, sand dollars, and many other forms of seashore life.

The boy from the interior of Canada, who knew nothing of the sea and its wonders, persuaded James to give him some of these marine specimens.

When Trevor returned to Peterborough with his microscope, his starfish, his clams, his bottles of diatoms, and his minerals, his parents were in despair. His "treasures" had long since overflowed the bureau drawers and chests in his room. Now they were spilling out of cartons and boxes all over the house. The maid complained that she could not sweep under the bed because the floors were covered with Trevor's collections.

When herbaria of pressed flowers, cases of insects impaled on pins, and boxes of minerals and fossils were piled in every room in the house, even decorating the parlor tables, Mrs. Kincaid called a halt. Trevor was so angry at his mother's disdain of his treasures that he built shelves in an unused part of the barn, and these too were soon overflowing.

Half-grudgingly, the doctor had an addition built to the barn to house the boxes and crates. "He is carrying this collecting too far," he complained to his wife. The Kincaids were beginning to realize that they had a most unusual son.

About this time, Dr. Kincaid, took Trevor to Ontario to attend a session of the Provincial Parliament, of which he was a member. At the close of the legislative session they went to Niagara Falls, where they visited not only an observatory where Trevor learned about the moon, but also a small museum. The exhibits so delighted him that his father had to drag him from the museum. As he was being ushered out of the museum, he said, "As soon as I get home, I'm going to have a museum of my own."

True to his word, the boy spent weeks preparing his collections for a public showing. When it was arranged to his satisfaction, he announced that he would hold an open house, to which anyone who wished to see the exhibition was welcome.

On the day of the showing, half the people in Peterborough came to see it and the unusual little boy who had arranged it. The visitors could hardly believe that such interesting and often beautiful materials had been found in the woods, the hills, the meadows, and the river near their town. In disgust, Trevor said, "People are so blind. They don't know that beauty is everywhere if they look for it." He seemed to have a special talent for seeing what no one else saw.

As one would expect of a boy whose energies were spent in investigating the world of nature, Trevor was a somewhat solitary lad. The boys in the neighborhood called him "Fossil," and sometimes laughed at him behind his back. They mimicked his long strides, and using their caps for insect nets, imitated his chasing bugs. He had the last laugh, however, when one of the boys, while making fun of him, was set upon and badly stung by a swarm of bees.

Yet in the rough and tumble of the boy's world, Trevor could hold his own, and often joined in the neighborhood games, somewhat absent-mindedly, to be sure.

"Come on, Fossil. Forget your bugs for a while. We want to play lacrosse and we need another man," urged Phil, who lived across the street from the Kincaids.

"Sure, I'll play." But, as usual, he suffered agonies while the all-important matter of choosing sides was going on. Would he be the last one picked? Today he was lucky and was tagged early. The racquets and balls were ready, and the game began. The score seesawed back and forth, first a point on one side and then on the other. Just when the winning point was about to be made, the ball was headed straight toward Trevor, but at that moment his attention was diverted from lacrosse to an eagle soaring across the sky overhead.

"Fossil, come down to earth. You're impossible, as dead as your silly specimens. You made us lose a point."

"Let's play another game. The eagle has probably flown away by this time," said Phil.

"If it isn't an eagle, Fossil will be looking at a snake or a spider. We can't win," grumbled Chuck.

In spite of their grumbling and their mimicking, the boys had a grudging admiration for the quiet, retiring boy, and sometimes felt inadequate in his presence. There was something determined, almost stubborn about him, and they realized that if pushed too far, he could get the better of them, in his own way.

Even if he could not play lacrosse or shinny, he could beat them all in skating and bobsledding. The sting of the snow and wind against his face made him laugh for joy. One summer a troupe of tumblers from a visiting circus became the neighborhood heroes. When Trevor, who was quick and agile, could turn two somersaults in the air in comparison with the one most of them could do, the boys gave him a hearty "hip-hip hurrah."

Tiring of acrobatics, he turned his attention to making a cannon from a gaspipe. "The first time the cannon exploded, my eyebrows were singed off, and the noise certainly impressed the boys," he later remembered.

Certainly his greatest accomplishment as a firearm expert came when he made bullets from the lead foil wrappings on packages of tea.

Unquestionably, Trevor's most useful boyhood accomplishment, and one that served him even in his old age, was learning to operate a printing press. By haunting a local printing office, Trevor's brother Morden had learned to operate the presses. Soon Morden had a small press of his own on which he printed a weekly sheet, *The Peterborough Star,* which he sold up and down the street for one cent. He also turned out posters, handbills, and business cards. The young entrepreneur hired Trevor as compositor, typesetter, clean-up boy, and messenger.

The high point of the boys' publishing adventure came on July 12, 1881, when James A. Garfield, President of the United States, was shot by a disgruntled office-seeker, Charles A. Guiteau. Up and down the street Trevor ran, shouting at the top of his voice, "President Garfield is shot! Shot! About to die!"

Still, nothing took the place of the farm in Trevor's life. Lying in the sunshine in a meadow of clover watching the bees gathering its sweetness, he was filled with love for every insect, bird, and plant that lived on the earth. In these wonders of nature he saw the handiwork of God.

How differently he felt toward God when he was warmed by the sun and uplifted by the songs of the birds than he did when sitting on a hard pew in the Methodist Church in Peterborough. Each Sunday morning the Kincaid children, thoroughly scrubbed and dressed in uncomfortable tight shoes, starched collars, and snugly buttoned coats, were marched off to church.

Exactly at eleven o'clock, parents and children filed into the family pew. The morning service began with the singing of "Nearer, My God, to Thee," "Jesus, Lover of My Soul" or "Work for the Night is Coming." The hymn was followed by a long, rambling prayer.

It was very hard for Trevor to keep his eyes closed and his feet from shuffling while these appeals to God were pouring from the preacher's mouth especially if a bird was singing in a tree outside the window. Then came the sermon, which most often was a warning of the judgment and torment waiting in the next world for those who strayed from the teachings of the church, or a scathing attack on the dangerous new theory of evolution. To Trevor, child that he was, the preacher's insistence that the earth was created in one week did not make sense. It took a radish seed more than a week to come through the ground, he knew.

After lustily singing "Onward, Christian Soldiers," and only half hearing the doxology, the Kincaid boys rushed out into the sunshine.

As a reward for good behavior during services, the family ate a dinner of roast beef, Yorkshire pudding, boiled potatoes, peas, fresh bread, jelly roll cake, and lemonade. Unfortunately, the tortures of the Sabbath were not yet over, for in the afternoon the children were sent off to Sunday School.

Even between Sunday School and evening service, boys were forbidden to play games or indulge in secular reading. Trevor's conscience troubled him for years for having tossed a ball against the walls of the barn one Sunday afternoon. And he was haunted by the experience of a bricklayer who was caught hoeing a patch of potatoes behind his house on Sunday afternoon. For this desecration, the workman was arrested and fined.

One day, as Trevor was walking down the street with a friend, the other boy suddenly stopped short and pointed to a man across the road and said in a hushed voice, "We must hurry. Do you see that man over there? He does not believe that what the Bible says about the creation of the earth is true. He believes in evolution. The preacher says that anyone who believes in evolution is going to be caught by the devil." The question of how the earth had been created began to bother Trevor.

Trevor had looked forward to going to school. He expected it would open up all kinds of wonders to him, but instead of being a happy experience, school took all of the joy out of his life. The Central School he attended was traditionally British with emphasis on Latin, Greek, history, and mathematics. Science and living languages were completely ignored.

Trevor disliked both the pompous headmaster and the subjects he was forced to study. Classes began at eight o'clock in the morning and lasted until late in the afternoon. The boy felt as though he were in prison. He agreed with Robert Browning that, "Long restraint chained down my soul." He no longer had time to wander in the fields, to peer under stones for insects, or even to read the books he loved.

Yet as a result of the stimulation of his home, his wide-open eyes, his questioning mind, and his knowledge of many branches of nature study, he was far more advanced than were most of his classmates, and by giving close attention to assignments and using his retentive memory, he passed from grade to grade in record time.

At the end of the seventh grade, the students took a test that was compiled and graded in the Provincial Education office in Toronto. Much to Trevor's surprise, he received the highest marks in the province among hundreds of competitors.

His friend Phil said, "Well, Fossil, guess your bug hunting and your reading paid off. Even if you can't play lacrosse, I'll bet you'll amount to something."

"I was just lucky," he modestly answered.

The Central School behind him forever, Trevor gave a whoop and headed for the farm, saying, "I'm free, free, free!" Dr. Kincaid was at a loss to know what kind of school would be best for his son. He had a shrewd suspicion that the headmaster of Central School or anyone of his ilk was not the one to cope with Trevor. Although he did not approve of the boy's everlasting collecting, he did not want to stifle his love of learning. The Collegiate Institute in Peterborough was also built on a narrow program of Greek, Latin, and philosophy, which he knew would not challenge the boy.

After a long search, the doctor discovered an Oxford graduate who had recently established a private school in town. Perhaps this school was the answer to the question of his son's further schooling. The Oxonian might be able to direct his interests into useful channels. Almost as soon as Trevor was enrolled in this new school, a fine rapport developed between him and the young teacher, who recognized that the boy had gifts and capabilities far beyond those of the average student.

The school was small and its program based on a modified tutorial program. The teacher gave Trevor much individual attention and tailored a course to his particular interests in biology, mathematics, and chemistry. He now became enthusiastic about school, where once he had hated it.

He particularly liked chemistry, working with acids, mercury, sulphur, and spirits of wine. He could produce all sorts of miracles with them. "Perhaps chemistry is the answer to his future career. I understand it will be an important field of study in the not too distant future," the doctor told his wife.

In the Oxford graduate's school, there was no competition for A's, B's, or C's, for 90's or 100's, or for any of the minute differences in achievement ratings, with their attendant heartbreaks and jealousies. In this tutorial system a student simply passed or failed.

Dr. Kincaid's practice was now so large that it kept him busy day and night—treating a boy with the measles; an elderly man suffering from rheumatism; a girl worried about her complexion; a woman giving birth to a baby. Patients who were able to walk came to the office in the center of town. Those who only thought they were sick and those whose ailments the doctor could not immediately diagnose were given large doses of "Aqua Pura," a concoction of water to which a little chocolate syrup has been added to give it a rich brown color and a pleasant taste. If the patient did not return to the doctor's office, or if he reported he was feeling better, the doctor concluded

"Aqua Pura" was an effective psychological remedy. If the patient sent word that his head or his stomach still ached or was worse than before, the doctor took a longer and more anxious look into the case.

The doctor hitched Nellie to the buggy and drove to the homes of the bedridden or seriously ill. For calls upon patients in the country, he hitched a pair of nicely matched bays to a surrey resplendent with a fringe on top. Trevor often accompanied his father on these long rides, sometimes in sun and warm breezes, sometimes in snow and darkness.

If the doctor did not need his son's help at a stop, and if the day was sunny and bright, the boy grabbed his collecting net and hustled off across the fields. More often, in a bleak kitchen with the patient wracked with pain and stretched out on a deal table, young Trevor held the flickering kerosene lamp so his father could see to splint a sprained ankle or to set the arm of a boy who had fallen from the ridgepole of a barn. Trevor, hating the sight of blood and the cries of pain, was determined he would never be a doctor.

To him, the best of these drives with his father were those taken on dark cold nights. Then with well-padded warming bricks tucked beneath the lap-robe, father and son, wearing knitted scarfs and overshoes and wrapped in heavy blankets, shared a feeling of closeness and companionship that they experienced at no other time.

On these drives, Dr. Kincaid, hoping to instill ancestral pride in his son, retold the long history of his family. Drawing the blankets closely around himself, he let the reins slacken so the horses could travel the familiar roads at their own speed.

The doctor always began by saying that the first landless ancestor of whom anything was known had moved to an estate near Campsie, Scotland in 1280. As was customary at that time, this humble man was called "Kyncade," the name of the estate to which he was attached, "Kyncade" in English meaning "wooded hill."

A century or more later, one of the Kincaids, following the banner of the Duke of Argyll and wearing the Campbell tartan, helped wrest Edinburgh Castle from the British. For this exploit he was made a Constable of the Castle and given extensive lands near Campsie. At the entrance to the property the Kincaids constructed a stone tower as a refuge from marauders.

In spite of the fierce antagonism between the clans of Scotland, the estate escaped serious destruction, and a new building was erected in 1690. In 1812 a still more commodious dwelling, Kincaid House, was built, the present home of Major John Kincaid.

"Have you seen it?" asked Trevor.

"No, my branch of the family emigrated to Ireland a couple of hundred years ago, but perhaps you can one day visit the homeland." The doctor was silent a long time, and he seemed lost in thought.

His mind coming back to the present, he slapped the reins over the backs of the horses and hurried on to the next patient, but through the frequent retelling of his family history, the doctor succeeded in instilling in his son's mind a lasting family loyalty.

Although Dr. Kincaid was a successful and prosperous physician, he was a poor businessman, who paid little attention to his financial interests. Perhaps through unwarranted faith in his fellow man, he fre-

quently signed notes that were never paid, or out of
sympathy for men's needs, he did not keep detailed
accountings or insist upon payment. In addition to
his misplaced confidence in his fellow men, he made
foolish investments. At this time, too, there were beginning to be evidences of a general decline in the
doctor's conduct. Whatever the reasons, things began to go badly for him.

The farm that had given Trevor complete happiness in his childhood was always an unprofitable in-
vestment, and the fine Georgian house the doctor
had hoped some day to construct on it was never
built. Too busy to give much personal attention to his
farm, he hired managers—in fact, a series of them—
each one taking advantage of the doctor's easygoing
ways. Each year the mortgage had to be increased
until it became an intolerable drain upon his resources, and he lost the farm.

After several other investments turned out badly,
the doctor owed large sums at the bank. About this
same time a bank official who had speculated with
the depositors' funds was sent to the penitentiary.
The new bank manager called for liquidation of all
outstanding notes. The beginning of the end had arrived for Dr. Kincaid. His creditors were not able to
pay their notes, and he found himself responsible for
far more money than he was able to raise. In a last
desperate attempt to meet some of the financial obli-
gations, he mortgaged the home in Peterborough in
which the family had lived for so long. Even this
could not save him. In a few months he found himself
bankrupt.

This was a crushing blow to the once highly respected and prosperous family. What could they do?
Dr. Kincaid decided to make a new start elsewhere.

He turned all his assets over to the bank and left for the United States.

Planning to send for his family as soon as he was settled in a new practice and a new country, he set out for California. On the train en route across Canada, he fell into conversation with a man who gave such glowing accounts of the Puget Sound country that the doctor felt sure that he could rebuild his practice and become wealthy there.

After visiting several towns in Washington Territory, Dr. Kincaid arrived in Olympia. The year was 1889. The Territory was about to become the state of Washington with Olympia as its capital. The town was bound to grow into a thriving city, everyone predicted. The price of land was skyrocketing, and new residential districts were being opened up far outside the town's limits. Dr. Kincaid decided that Olympia was just the place he had been looking for. Prospects for both his medical practice and profits from real estate ventures seemed limitless.

After he had lived a few months in Olympia, he sent for Trevor, thinking the boy could make himself useful around the building he was remodeling in the center of town to serve both as an office and as living quarters.

Thus it was that Trevor Kincaid, a boy of 16, slight of stature, and full of curiosity about the world, left the progressive school and Peterborough in August, 1889, and set out by rail for Vancouver, half a continent away. To him that journey was a passport to a new life. Everything was exciting: the speed at which the train traveled, the medley of passengers with their strange speech and dress, the ever-changing landscape, the great rolling plains, the wooded hillsides, the lakes. But it was the snow-covered moun-

tains that particularly held his wonder. Their great
bulk surpassed in grandeur anything he had
dreamed of. A verse he had learned in Sunday School
flashed across his mind: "The heavens declare the
glory of God and the firmament showeth His handiwork"; surely these great mountains were God's
handiwork.

At Banff, surrounded as it was by immense, snow-
capped peaks, Trevor felt he had been transplanted
into a fairyland. During the train's half-hour stop
there, he tried to see everything: the great hotel,
Lake Louise tucked high on a mountain, the village
itself. But he was suddenly brought back to stern
reality. The train had gone off without him. It was not
the mountains that had brought disaster to the young
man; it was the sight of a man selling specimens of
minerals.

Unable to stifle his collecting instinct, Trevor had
stopped to bargain for some shiny pink quartz. While
he was haggling about the price of the quartz, to his
shocked surprise he saw the train almost out of sight
far down the tracks. His heart seemed to drop out of
his body. He had lost not only his train, but also his
luggage.

Only for a moment, however, was the boy daunted
by his first setback in the big outside world. He hurried to the station-master and told him his story. Realizing the dismay of the youthful traveler, the
station-master made arrangements for him to ride a
freight train that was following close behind the passenger train. Thus it came about that, perched high
in the caboose, Trevor came through some of the
finest scenery in North America from the vantage
point of an early-day private Vistadome car. Somewhere along the line, his goods and chattels had been

taken off the passenger train and dumped on a platform for the freight train to pick up.

Even greater than his amazement at seeing the mountains was his first glimpse of the Strait of Georgia at Vancouver. Was he really seeing the ocean, that fascinating, mysterious, incomprehensible body of water of which his cousin, James Potts, had told him?

With his battered suitcase and his newly purchased pink quartz clutched in his hand, he ran to a hotel near the railroad station to put up for the night. The enchanted traveler dropped his bags in the middle of the room and rushed down to the shore to see, taste, touch, and smell the great body of water about which he knew so little.

The next morning, still wide-eyed and bewildered by the new world about him, he hurried down to the docks to take the Canadian Pacific steamer for Tacoma. The foghorns, the whistles of the ferryboats, the barges loading with lumber, and trawlers unloading three-foot salmon made his head whirl. Reluctantly, he left the fascinating activities of the waterfront and boarded the boat, which wound its way between islands lying like jewels in Puget Sound.

In Tacoma he transferred to a small steamer, the *Fleetwood,* for the trip to Olympia. In an hour he would see his father. What would his new home be like? Would it be home without his mother? Would he have books to read and a school to attend? His father had written that although Olympia might seem rough and primitive in comparison with the established community of Peterborough, it would offer Trevor unlimited avenues of investigation, and perhaps the opportunity to earn some money. (He said nothing about the area opening up new collecting grounds.) In any case, the boy knew another exciting adventure lay ahead.

The *Fleetwood* was nearing the dock in Olympia. The approach to the town was anything but impressive, for the sprawling village was situated nearly at the south end of Puget Sound, where the water became shallower and shallower until it ended in mud flats extending a mile beyond the town.

Trevor paid little attention to all this. His concern was to find the familiar figure of his father in the motley group of dudes, loggers, fishermen, and drifters standing idly on the docks. And then he saw him, the tall man dressed as he always had been, in a wide slouch hat, Prince Albert coat, a luxuriant growth of whiskers covering the lower part of his face.

The moment the gangplank was raised, Dr. Kincaid was on the boat, a protective arm around his son's shoulders, a welcoming smile on his face, and a strong arm to carry the bags.

"You have grown. We must buy you some new pants," he said, adding, "Hungry, son? Let's go and have a plate of Olympia pan oysters."

"Oysters? Do they grow around here?"

"Indeed they do. And no one can fry them like the Chinese cook at Doane's Oyster House."

Trevor had reached his new home in the United States.

CHAPTER 2

Life in
Pioneer Olympia

THE OYSTERS SERVED at Doane's Oyster House that
night were the most delicious food Trevor had ever
tasted. He never forgot their intriguing flavor. Years
later he wondered if that first meal in Olympia was
prophetic of how much of his life would be involved
in the study of that gourmet food.

Leaving the oyster house, father and son walked to
a sprawling, unpainted building at the intersection of
Main and Water Streets where, on the second floor
above a drygoods store, Dr. Kincaid had his office.
Next to the office was a large unfinished room, which
he planned to partition into living quarters for his
family.

The next morning Trevor's heart sank as he looked
at the uncared-for structure crowded between
equally ugly buildings. Everywhere he looked was a
forest of tree stumps with muddy, rutty roads running between them. Every third building in the
town was a saloon, an eating house, a bawdy theatre,
or a real estate office. Was that where his father expected to make a fortune? he asked himself. How
different it was from the comfortable house he had
left in Peterborough with its wide streets lined with
spreading elms and bright flowers.

The appearance of the town did not depress the
boy for long, however, for he was soon caught up in

the excitement that was gripping Olympia, which on November 11th was to become the capital of the new state of Washington. Of all the preparations being made for that important event, the feature that most impressed the sixteen-year-old boy was the banner strung across the speaker's platform on which was written the Chinook legend: *"Quanisum mukutty cheechaca alki"* ("There isn't much here now, but there will be by and by").

As Trevor stood outside the building in which his father had his office, he watched the covered wagons pull into town, bringing hundreds of transients. Olympia was in the midst of a land boom caused largely by the high hopes of the new state, the general Western trek, and the completion of the Northern Pacific Railroad to Tacoma. Tracts of stump land and wild forest areas were being plotted into town sites at great distances from Olympia and sold at fabulous prices. It was hard for him to envision the great city that would rise here by and by!

Dr. Kincaid, along with other speculators, bought and sold large tracts of land sight unseen. With each transfer of ownership the prices soared; the purchasers seldom bothered to visit their newly acquired properties.

The boom gave Dr. Kincaid an opportunity, so he thought, to double or treble the fortune he had lost in Peterborough. All went well for a time, but inevitably, as even young Trevor realized it would, the crash came in 1890, and the doctor found himself with deeds to lots that were not worth the paper on which they were written.

Even as far away as Massachusetts, news of the fabulous growth of Olympia had spread. Hazard Stevens, son of Isaac Stevens, the first Territorial Governor of Washington, dreaming of handsome profits, decided to cash in on a large piece of land his father had bought many years before.

Since young Stevens was unwilling to place his land in the hands of a real estate dealer or to pay rent for an office, he set up a tent equipped with a table, a couple of chairs, and a map of the land and hired 17-year-old Trevor Kincaid to run the office while he showed the land to prospective buyers.

But by the time Stevens had arrived in Olympia, the land boom was beginning to slow down, so he sold few plots. While waiting for customers to come to the tent, the office boy made an intensive study of a nest of mound-building ants just behind the tent, and he discovered that the woods around his new home were filled with all sorts of fascinating plants and animals.

Disappointed in his real estate venture, Stevens returned to Boston. Trevor Kincaid found himself in the ranks of the unemployed. But he could hardly wait to investigate this luxuriant world of nature.

Much of the countryside was logged-off land, grim and depressing. Yet in spite of man's efforts to destroy the beauty of the natural world, Trevor looked in awe at the hundred-foot-high cedar and fir trees and found countless kinds of plants struggling up between the burned and denuded stumps. Birds hopped about among the discarded branches that covered the ground, while insects crawled everywhere. To him it was a glimpse of Eden.

In the comparatively mild climate of Western Washington, he found salal, Oregon grape, and ferns growing all winter. No wonder the new state was being called the "Evergreen State," he thought, as he looked at the sword ferns and huckleberry in their bright green foliage.

As the days lengthened and spring came to the dark forests, Trevor grew ecstatic at the sight of the rainbow colors of the rhododendron, wild currant, and solomon seal. Beautiful, too, were the ocean spray, fire weed, Indian paint-brush, flax, mock orange, and everlasting flower, which brightened the trails during the summer. In the autumn he feasted his eyes on Michaelmas daisies, vine maple, and sumac, as they made their last salute to the dying year, and as maples and alders painted the hillsides with gold and crimson. The doctor still did not approve of his son's excessive interest in collecting, but inasmuch as Olympia did not offer a suitable school for him to attend, he tolerated Trevor's childish activity.

One day, while walking through the logged-off countryside, Trevor came upon a grove of oak trees. Among the oaks were thimble berries covered with galls, abnormal growths caused by insects. Unfamiliar with these strange growths on plants, the embryo scientist gathered a number of them and sent them to the only scientist whose name he knew, Professor C. P. Gillette of the University of Colorado, who discovered several new species among them. One of these he named *Diastrophus kincaidii*, the first of a long line of species named in Trevor's honor.

This recognition of his work excited young Kincaid. He subscribed to an entomological magazine in which he read that Eastern scientists were eager to receive insects from the Northwest United States. He spent hours each day collecting material to send to zoologists: spiders to Dr. Nathan Banks at Cornell

University and to Dr. William Ashmead of the American Museum; bees to Dr. T. D. A. Cockerell of Colorado; butterflies to Dr. Henry Skinner of the Philadelphia Academy. As thanks for a collection of insects, Dr. Alexander Macgillavray sent Kincaid a copy of the outlines used in his course in entomology at Cornell. Trevor took it as an extension course.

These men had no idea that the avid collector was a boy of 17; they addressed him as "Professor" and honored him in many ways. During the years 1890–1894, Trevor made a personal collection of 60,000 insects, in addition to sending 100,000 specimens to scientists in all parts of the United States.

To increase the range of his collecting, he made longer and longer trips into the foothills of the Cascade Mountains. Hearing that fossils might be found around Tenino, where there was a large quarry, Trevor set out one morning at daybreak on a twenty-mile hike. To his disappointment, he found that the material being quarried there was gravel, the result of the whole region having been overlaid with glacial caps. At the end of a long, unsuccessful day of fossil hunting, he took from his knapsack a sandwich and an apple and threw himself down on a bed of moss and pine needles. The fragrance of the woods, the twitter of birds, and the mystery of the stars lulled him to sleep.

Soon Trevor Kincaid's boyish figure striding across the meadows or darting in or out of the woods became a familiar sight around Olympia. Most of the time he walked alone, his mind busy with many things, his eyes catching sight of the tiniest insect at his feet. In a short time he was able to recognize and name hundreds of species of plants and animals around his new home.

Of course, Trevor had expected to attend school in Olympia, but at that time only a fourth of the school districts in the state gave instruction beyond the eighth grade, and much of it was pretty poor. Although there was a high school of sorts in Olympia, Dr. Kincaid decided his son would be wasting his time attending it. He was certainly more advanced in literature, science, and mathematics than were the local students, and without doubt his knowledge of the world in general was far wider than theirs. With the few dollars Trevor had earned sitting in the makeshift land office, he bought Livy's history of Rome, translating it from Latin to English. He also bought a physics textbook, but without experimental apparatus found the study of physics unsatisfying.

To fill the bleak rainy days when he could not wander through the woods, Trevor acted as office boy for his father, built partitions in the big room that was to serve as a home for the family, and put up shelves and cupboards to hold his mother's silver and dishes. He had no desire to mingle with the men who frequented the pool halls and taverns, so he was at a loss to know how to pass the long evenings. How he longed for books, that wonderful solace of the lonely. Because there was no town library in Olympia, this world of the mind was closed to him. Even his father's medical books were not available, for he had left all but the most essential ones in Peterborough.

One day while rummaging through the frame Capitol Building, however, he discovered a shelf of reference books, government documents, and law books. The librarian told him they were for the use of state officials and members of the legislature and could not be taken from the building. Trevor had little interest in these fields, but he was so happy to see books, regardless of their subject matter, that he returned to the library several times, hoping to find a few volumes on other subjects. He discovered several dust-covered volumes on botany by Hooker and Nuttall tucked away on a top shelf.

Eagerly he lifted them from the shelf, wiped off the dust, and hurried to the librarian, who insisted they could not be taken from the building. Then seeing the boy's disappointment and realizing that the shy, mild-mannered young man with the springy step and hearty laugh was no ordinary drifter, she made a great concession and allowed him to take several volumes home. From that day Trevor spent the long evenings reading everything from constitutional law to botany.

The meeting with the librarian in the Capitol Building was a memorable day for Trevor, for it led to many valuable contacts. A library maintained by the Masonic Lodge opened its doors to him, as did several private book collectors. He formed the habit of dropping into the bookstore to chat with Mr. Balleau, the store manager, who had recently organized a study group. When he was invited to join the group, Trevor felt a great honor had come to him, because through it he came to know most of the educated people in Olympia.

Because he was much younger than the other members of the group, he hesitated at first to express his ideas. His enthusiasm endeared him to the older members, however, and when the talk turned to natural history, everyone deferred to his opinions. As the months passed, he lost his shyness and took part in the discussions of a wide range of subjects. He later said that much of his finest training came from this group.

One day Mr. Balleau handed Trevor a book asking, "Are you acquainted with the publications of the Humboldt Library?"

"No, what are they?"

"Inexpensive paperback editions of standard works in science, philosophy, economics, literature," answered Mr. Balleau. "For instance, you can buy a copy of Darwin's *Origin of Species* for thirty cents."

Trevor had found a source of information far more valuable than a high school course of study could have been. For months he spent every cent he could get his hands on for Humboldt editions. His reading became so diversified that through the paperback books he gained a liberal education.

One afternoon when Kincaid was returning a book to the Capitol library, the librarian said, "By the way, Mr. Kincaid, a gentleman was here yesterday asking about the young man who was reading books on botany."

"Botany?" asked Trevor. (He didn't think there was anyone in town but himself who cared about botany.) "Who was he?" he inquired.

"Henderson—L. F. Henderson. He is working in his brother's abstracting office."

As fast as his legs could carry him, the boy hurried to the office. Mr. Henderson, a graduate of Cornell University with a major in botany, had taught in Portland for a couple of years; now he was helping his brother and botanizing in the Olympia area. At once the man and the boy put their heads together, poring over plants in Henderson's herbaria. The next weekend they set out for Bush Prairie, a botanist's paradise, coming home with so many plants that it took them weeks to identify and mount them. Trevor Kincaid had found a kindred spirit.

Almost two years had passed since Dr. Kincaid had left Peterborough, and his letters to his wife were becoming more and more infrequent. She was becoming impatient at her husband's delay in sending for her and her daughter. Was the fortune in real estate he had talked about so glibly only a dream, or did he not want her to come to Olympia? At her insistence, the doctor somewhat reluctantly sent for the family. For the first few months they lived in the improvised quarters above the drygoods store, but the ugly cramped rooms strained the tempers of both husband and wife, and Mrs. Kincaid found little in common with the women in Olympia. Although the town was still crowded with transients, the doctor was able to rent a house. When the familiar furnishings were in place, Trevor felt happier than he had been since arriving in the United States, but the relations between his parents did not improve much. Another daughter, Airdrie, was born.

Dr. Kincaid retained his office near the center of town, often staying away from home for days. It was necessary, he maintained, for the office to be accessible day and night to the floating population that poured through the town.

Frequently Trevor accompanied his father to logging camps, oyster-farming operations, or fishing boats to treat men injured in these hazardous occupations. At best, the help the doctor could give was rudimentary, because of the absence of adequate hospitals and surgical instruments in this pioneer country, but the men had great faith in his ability to help them. While his father was busy with his patients, his son watched the oystermen harvest their crops or loggers fell a tree.

Finally, the doctor said, "You had better find a job. All you do is collect bugs or watch other men work.

You will never be able to make a living the way you are going."

So Trevor got a job as a stake artist, helping to survey for the Northern Pacific Railroad between Olympia and Port Townsend. Quickly, through his winning personality, his modesty, his candor, and his hearty laugh, he established happy relations with his fellow workers.

His duties as a stake artist were to cut off lengths of cedar logs and to split them into flat stakes pointed at one end. These he dumped into a gunny sack, which he slung on his back. At distances indicated by the transit men, he drove the stakes into the ground. He also marked the cuts and fills selected by the levelers. This work suited him perfectly because, without neglecting his duties, he was able to drop many interesting insects into the cyanide bottle he carried in his pocket. After several weeks of this work, he was promoted to making mathematical computations for the guidance of surveyors leveling the roadway.

When the Olympia end of the railroad was completed, Trevor left the railroad gang, but not before he had been dubbed "professor," had made a number of friends, and had filled a dozen insect cases with specimens.

Without question, the position least to young Kincaid's liking and talent was clerking in a hardware store owned by Robert Frost, a friend of his father. With his usual preparation for any work he undertook, Trevor dutifully studied wholesale hardware catalogs to learn the weights and lengths of nails, the kinds and shapes of hinges, the types of saws and picks used in the woods. He also dispensed pots and pans, chose chimneys to fit any lamp, demonstrated saws and axes, and learned to tie packages neatly (quite an art in itself, he found).

The entire day centered around his lunch hour, for the minute the clock struck twelve, he grabbed his coat and headed for the woods, where he kept an insect net hidden in the hollow of a tree.

After several months it became evident both to Mr. Frost and to Trevor that he was not cut out to be a hardware clerk. A few days before he left the store for good, Mr. Frost, who had been celebrating the Fourth of July by drinking with his cronies, staggered into the store. There sat his assistant, absorbed in drawing geometrical figures on a piece of wrapping paper. Frost snatched off his hat, bowed low, and said, "My boy, one day we will all be taking off our hats to you."

Unknown to Frost, many a customer had carried home lampshades or hinges wrapped in paper covered with algebraic formulas or Latin translations, with which the young salesman had amused himself while waiting for customers. He could not endure being idle. Trevor left the hardware store and business life forever. Out of his meager wages of ten dollars a month, he had set aside a few nickels and dimes each week toward his further education.

His dreams of becoming wealthy through real estate blasted, Dr. Kincaid began to look about for other ways to get rich. He was now carried away by a scheme presented to him by a Mr. Cardwell, whom he had known in Canada. This old "friend" appeared in Olympia and persuaded the doctor that they could make their fortunes by capturing sea otters off Gray's Harbor. By asking a few questions, the doctor could have found that no sea otters had been killed off the Washington coast for many years and that in any case, they were extremely difficult to capture. But believing Mr. Cardwell implicitly, he outfitted a crew of men with high-powered guns and invested several thousand dollars in boats for otter catching.

As everyone had predicted, no sea otters were caught, and the venture came to an inglorious end. When his son remonstrated with him about this impractical business scheme, the doctor answered, "John D. Rockefeller didn't make his money with six per cent interest. He made bold investments and took daring risks. Why shouldn't I?"

Mr. Cardwell now knew of a deal that was a "sure thing." A fine stand of timber on the Skokomish River in Mason County could be bought for a "song." He persuaded the doctor to finance the purchase, assuring him the timber could be logged off at handsome profits.

Again without seeking advice, Dr. Kincaid plunged into the scheme. A logging outfit to be known as Cardwell's Camp was established on the Skokomish River about sixteen miles from Shelton. A large log building was constructed for a bunk and mess hall. A crew of twenty-five men, mostly of Scottish and Irish ancestry, was hired and six yoke of oxen purchased. Cardwell was to manage the camp. A short time after logging got underway, one of the workers made a trip to Olympia on foot to tell the doctor the camp was being badly managed. Matters came to a climax soon afterwards, when Cardwell sold all movable supplies and absconded with the money. The men had not been paid, the oxen were half-starved, and there was no one to direct the work.

In desperation, the doctor ordered Trevor to go to the camp and hold things together. For a long time the boy resisted his father's order, but because of his persistent urgings and his love for him, he went to the Skokomish. The camp was in a state of utter confusion, but with the help of an intelligent foreman, they managed to get operations underway again. Trevor insisted that his father hire a competent manager. This he refused to do.

As a result of this fiasco, a 19-year-old boy utterly inexperienced in logging or the handling of men found himself in charge of an operation involving many thousands of dollars, keeping the time of the men, paying them a token share of their wages, ordering meat and vegetables and other supplies from neighboring settlers, negotiating for additional tracts of timber, and keeping the books in order.

When the myriad other jobs had been taken care of, Trevor also became assistant cook, cutting up quarters of beef, peeling bushels of potatoes, boiling great pots of beans, flipping mountains of hotcakes, baking dozens of loaves of bread, and brewing gallons of coffee. He had heard that the way to keep loggers happy and on the job was to feed them well. If that would do the trick, he decided he would keep their stomachs full, even if their pocketbooks were empty.

Like most of the logging outfits in the early 1890's, the Kincaid operation was carried on almost entirely by human strength and by oxen. A team of twelve oxen was required to drag the logs from the woods, and only a teamster with a lot of skill and much profanity could manage the great beasts. The Kincaid teamster possessed both these qualifications, which, with the aid of a strong goad, the oxen seemed to understand. The ox driver was also the kingpin of the crew, earning a hundred dollars a month, a fantastic salary for those days.

To avoid being dubbed "professor" on this job, Trevor called himself "Ted." One of his first duties as a real woodsman was to oversee the building of a skid road over which the logs could be dragged from the logging areas to the river bank. The loggers built the road by laying logs horizontally over the soggy ground to furnish traction for the ox teams to move across. The swampers cleared away the brush and debris around the trees to be felled. The sawyers next cut notches in the tree trunk about six feet from the ground to direct the fall of the tree. They then cut through the tree at that height with a crosscut saw, and it crashed to the ground with terrific force. Many a logger had lost his life by being struck by the branches—"widow-makers" they were called—and Trevor was haunted lest one of his men suffer such a fate. When the tree had been felled, the trunk was cut into lengths suitable for hauling, usually thirty feet, leaving behind tremendous waste. The logs were chained together length-wise, hauled by the oxen over the skid road to the river bank and dumped into the stream. Here they waited, sometimes for months, for high water to carry them down to the mill, where they would be offered for sale.

Trevor had hoped to get his logs out of the river in June when the melting snows in the Olympic Mountains and the spring rains usually sent the rivers surging. In 1893, because high water did not come in June, the logs lay in the river until December, when a warm "Chinook" wind melted the snow in the Olympics, causing the water to rush headlong down the mountain sides, carrying with it everything in its path. With a roar like the explosion of a cannon, the log boom broke, the logs beating and bumping against one another in wild confusion. The force of the water was so great that the Skokomish River surged high over its banks, scattering logs through nearby meadows and woods.

To Trevor the scattering of the logs was a staggering blow, for there was almost no money to carry on the logging operations. It would be necessary to add debt to debt by employing men and teams to roll the logs back into the river and to raft them into booms. What was even worse, by the time the logs were marketed, the price had dropped from six dollars a thousand feet to three dollars. Disaster was staring Dr. Kincaid in the face again.

The loggers worked at the back-breaking job from dawn to dark six days a week. By the end of the day, they were so weary that the minute they had eaten dinner, they dropped onto their sawdust mattresses and slept. Gabriel's horn could not have awakened them, although the smell of flapjacks the next morning did. To offset the hard work, on Saturday nights the men gambled and drank away their meager earnings.

With each month the financial condition of the Kincaid logging operation worsened. After a year, it was evident it could not hold out longer. As a last gesture of good will to the defunct company, the settlers gave a big dance in a neighboring camp to which everyone within twenty miles came.

In preparation for the party, the men in the Kincaid camp bathed either by plunging into the icy river or by daubing their bodies with water heated in pans on the kitchen stove. Laughing and joking about the hearts they would break, they shaved, brushed and oiled their hair, and put on clean plaid wool shirts and fresh pairs of pants held high by strong suspenders.

After trudging a mile or two through the logged-off forests, they reached the scene of the party where, to the accompaniment of a scratchy fiddle, they stomped through square dances and polkas with such violence that it seemed the walls must collapse. When the merriment was at its height, Trevor was tempted to join the revellers, but stored far back in his memory were the admonitions of the Methodist minister in Peterborough on the evils of dancing.

What stories the men told during the following week of the huge servings of venison and the number of pieces of blackberry pie they ate. But to Trevor the most hilarious tales were of their escapades— Jack falling flat on the floor after stumbling over his partner's long dress; Jim taking his sweetie outdoors to cool off; Tom having had a bit too much to drink and falling asleep in a corner of the dance floor; Pete making eyes at a farmer's wife and then worrying lest he get a bullet in the back for his boldness. Scarcely a man in camp escaped the ribbing of his friends for some breach of loggers' etiquette.

Finally the camp was shut down. The closing of the camp made little difference to the loggers, for most of them were drifters, rarely staying more than a few months with one outfit; then they were off to more productive areas.

Trevor returned to Olympia as soon as the equipment was disposed of, vowing that his operation of logging camps and business ventures was over forever. In his *Autobiography* he wrote of his logging experiences: "Although it would seem at first sight that my time had been wasted, I have never regretted that year. I learned a lot about human nature, methods of conducting business and the techniques of handling men. It definitely took me out of my ivory tower."

Several months after the logging operations were shut down, Kincaid, on one of his rambles, encountered two of his former men, who were hand-logging. They invited him to share their camp for the night, a crude tent thrown up on the edge of the woods. To celebrate Ted's visit, one of the men robbed a henhouse in a nearby Indian reservation and prepared a big kettle of chicken stew. Because the night was cold and the men had only one blanket, Ted was wedged tightly between the two big, hairy, lumberjacks, from which vantage point he was forced to listen to their loud snoring. Characteristically making the best of the situation, he shrugged, "That was probably better than sleeping under a tree on a cold night."

Soon after he was back in Olympia, he and Henderson, knapsacks and plant presses on their backs, set out and wandered happily through the woods and along the streams. Trevor turned the collections of plants he had made in the logging camp over to Henderson, who used them in an exhibit of Washington State flowers at the World's Fair in Chicago in 1893. Many of the plants were later included in herbaria and sent to Washington State College and to the University of Washington.

Through his association with Henderson, Trevor became convinced that he must continue his education, but without money and with meager preparation, he was at a loss as to where he might get the training he needed. Henderson told him that C. W. Piper, who had recently been asked to organize a Department of Botany at the State Agricultural College in Pullman, had been trained by Orson Bennett Johnson at the University of Washington. Although Piper was primarily a botanist, he was also well informed about insects, and Henderson felt Piper would be able to help Trevor with his plans to go back to school.

On Piper's next visit to Olympia, he called on Trevor and recommended he get in touch with Johnson, who was "One of the most inspiring men I ever met," he said. The prospect of this contact so excited Kincaid that he took the steamer to Seattle the next day to meet Johnson. Immediately he was caught under the spell of the professor's personality. Johnson gave the young scientist a most cordial reception and assured him the deficiencies in his training could be made up. He spent two days talking with Johnson and looking over his immense collection of insects and beetles. Then and there the two men became fast friends, a friendship that lasted until the end of Johnson's life twenty years later.

More valuable to Kincaid, perhaps, than his meeting with Johnson was being asked to speak before a meeting of the Young Naturalists' Society, a group of young men interested in many phases of nature study. At the close of Kincaid's remarks, a motion was made and seconded to suspend the rules and proceed to elect him as a corresponding member. Then it was stated that he was about to remove to Seattle and to become an active member of the Society, whereupon the motion was withdrawn.

Kincaid returned to Olympia resolved to enroll in the University of Washington and to associate himself immediately with Johnson and the Young Naturalists. He could scarcely wait to pack his trunk and his collections and begin life as a student. Through his numerous jobs, Trevor had saved one hundred dollars, which he felt sure would see him through the first year at the University.

A few days before he was to set out upon his great adventure, word came from his brother in New York that his wife had died, leaving two young children. Morden asked his mother to come to care for them. Since Dr. Kincaid insisted he had no money to finance the journey, the only solution was for Trevor to give his mother the money he had so carefully saved. His bank account was gone, and with it his hopes of becoming a university student.

CHAPTER 3

A Conditioned Freshman

Trevor Kincaid was the most disappointed young man in Olympia when the shade was drawn on the window that promised him an education. Yet he determined he would not let the loss of a hundred dollars swerve him from his plan to return to school. He knew the time was right for him to leave Olympia. His mother and sisters were in New York; his father had been at cross purposes with his family for some time and was living in rooms adjacent to his office. Trevor was alone in the family home. No one would miss him.

He was certain his destiny lay in the world of science, and to pursue that goal he must have an education. Even if Seattle were small and crude and the University scarcely more than a preparatory school, they offered him the only opportunity of getting to college, and his meeting with Professor Johnson and the Young Naturalists had convinced him he could find inspiration and intellectual stimulus there.

To Trevor it seemed most fortunate that there was a university of any kind in Seattle; the Territorial University had been established, at least on paper, just five years after the first white settlers had come to Seattle.

The town was then a drab, ugly village of perhaps twenty families and a hundred or two unmarried men. The houses were crude log cabins or frame buildings without paint or plaster. Charles Gates in his book, *The First Hundred Years of the University of Washington,* wrote that in 1855 the tiny frontier settlement of Seattle was perhaps the loneliest of civilization's outposts. The most important place in the town was Henry Yesler's sawmill and cookhouse, which served as a public gathering place:

> Here most of the men in town earned their money; here ships came for cargoes and discharged their groceries. The puffing, buzzing and heaving of steam from the sawmill made the music of the bay, and the hum of the saws was the undertone of each household. By its whistle all the clocks in the village were regulated and the whole of its business carried on.

With faith in the meaning of the Chinook legend, "Quanisum mukutty cheechaca alki" ("There isn't much here now, but there will be by and by"), a group of men sitting in Yesler's mill in the middle 1850's suggested, more or less in jest, no doubt, that a university would give Seattle the "cultural tone" she needed and be a first step in her becoming a great city. Too, the remark might have been made with the vague hope that a university would bring a federal grant and other benefits to the isolated village. It seems unrealistic that anyone could have expected the idea of a university in Seattle to be taken seriously. Yet Isaac Stevens, the Territorial Governor, suggested it to the legislature, which enacted a law on January 29, 1855, providing that "The University of Washington shall be and hereby is located and established in Seattle and the County of King." Governor Stevens immediately asked for a federal grant, saying, "The subject of education already occupies the minds and hearts of the people of the Territory."

Of course the area was not ready for a university. There were almost no schools in the Territory. The Territorial Superintendent of Schools, B. C. Lippincott, remarked with some asperity, "There are not in King County one hundred children of lawful age to attend even a district school, and one might well wonder if there were a single young man in the whole of the State of Washington who could pass an examination to enter a university course. Who then would go to the Territorial University, if one should be established?"

Yet the idea did not die. It was a beautiful dream, a "phantom in a wooded wilderness." Nevertheless, after much political trading, frequent reorganization, and some financial irregularities, the Commissioners for the University on February 9, 1861, determined to get its share of federal grants by making the university a reality.

Certainly it seemed a forlorn hope. Neither Seattle (with a population of 302, excluding Indians) nor the sparsely settled Territory had a single quality to recommend it as the site for a university. That is, nothing except hope—that magic word that drove pioneers on to do the impossible. Once having set their hand to the task, they elected the Reverend Daniel Bagley President of the University and President of the Board of Regents, and authorized him to act for the Board in the construction of a building. At once the Reverend Mr. Bagley persuaded Arthur Denny, one of the founders of Seattle, to give eight acres of his claim, known as "The Knoll," a beautiful eminence facing Elliott Bay for a campus (now the site of the Olympic Hotel).

Another two acres were donated by Charles and Mary Terry and Edward Lander. A white frame colonial building 50 X 85 feet, with a bell tower and a handsome portico supported by four Ionic columns, was planned. To speed the construction of the building, many prominent citizens of Seattle wielded hammers and saws, picks and shovels. President Bagley himself, who had once been a carpenter, was drafted to help with the flooring, shingling, and painting.

The formal opening of the University was planned for September, 1861. During the summer of that year, Asa Mercer traveled 400 miles in a canoe paddled by two Indians (water was the sole highway in the new country). They visited every logging camp and fishing village from Bellingham to Olympia, trying to persuade young men to enter the school. Mercer persuaded a dozen students to enroll only after he promised them jobs on Saturdays cutting cordwood.

When the University opened its doors, some thirty primary and high school children were on hand. Asa Mercer and Virginia Calhoun taught all the classes. One student, Clarence Bagley, son of the President, enrolled for college work. By 1865 there were still only five persons in school trained for work on the college level. Until 1875 the University was financed solely from tuition fees of five dollars and profits from the operation of the "boarding house." Several times during the next decade the University was forced to close. Even as late as 1881, it seemed the University must perish. In 1893, thirty-two years after its founding, five persons were in the graduating class.

Such, in general, were the conditions at the University of Washington in 1894 when Trevor Kincaid packed his old-fashioned trunk and borrowed a hand-cart, on which he loaded 65,000 insects and plants, and placed them on a steamer for Seattle. Before leaving Olympia he called at his father's office to say goodbye and to ask if he would help finance his education. The doctor put his hand in his pocket, took out a ten-dollar gold piece, and gave it to his son with his blessing.

Trevor knew that henceforth he was on his own. The only money he had in addition to the shiny gold piece was two silver dollars. One of these he needed for his boat fare to Seattle; the other he put in his back pocket as insurance toward getting back to Olympia if he could not find work. After arriving in Seattle, he began pushing the cart containing his insects up the hill to the University.

He did not feel particularly discouraged in regard to finances, for Professor Johnson had assured him that many students worked their way through school by splitting firewood, carrying newspapers, mowing lawns, and tending furnaces in private homes. The University had recently suspended the five-dollar tuition fee it had originally charged, because the school was desperate for students. To get them there was the important thing.

The campus, Kincaid recalled later, consisted of four buildings: The handsome colonial main hall, East Hall, which housed the kitchen and dining room; North Hall, a two-story frame dormitory; the President's cottage; and a three-story frame building occupied by the Young Naturalists' Society. When Trevor reached the campus that first Sunday in September, it was practically deserted; his room in North Hall was not ready for occupancy nor was the dining hall in operation. Ralph Nichols, a former stu-

The Territorial University was built in 1861 on the "knoll." The President's house is in the background.

Seattle in 1894 when Trevor Kincaid enrolled as a conditioned freshman in the University of Washington. The Territorial University stands on a hill in the upper left.

dent, seeing Trevor wandering aimlessly about the dormitory, invited the newcomer to bunk with him until his room was available.

That evening Trevor was very hungry, but he hardly dared think of spending any of the precious gold piece for food. Nichols, no doubt sensing Kincaid's dilemma, suggested they eat at a restaurant on Pike Street where they could get a hearty meal for fifteen cents, including a piece of apple pie. The meal, served at a long table covered with a far from clean red-and-white checkered tablecloth, consisted of boiled potatoes, great hunks of beef, cabbage, coffee, and all the bread and butter they could eat— and the pie. Nichols, by chucking the waitress under the chin and indulging in a mild flirtation, persuaded her to bring each of them a second piece of pie.

The room in North Hall assigned to Trevor and his roommate, Harry Traeger, a farm boy from Puyallup, was unplastered and completely unfurnished. For a while it looked as if they would have to sleep on the floor. Then someone tipped them off that under the building were odds and ends of boards that might be made into a bedframe. They were soon ransacking the discards under North Hall. Boards of almost every length and width were available. The bed frame the boys made was far from artistic, but it was a bed of sorts. The matter of a mattress was not so easy to solve. The best Trevor could devise was to lay boards across the bed frame and spread his blankets over them; his up-ended trunk served as a bedside table, and a box filled with insects answered for a chair. The roommates pooled their resources and bought a kerosene lamp for forty cents.

Housekeeping in North Hall was a simple matter. Once a week Trevor swept the litter from the floor of his room into the hallway; then a boy down the corridor whisked the accumulated debris to the end of the hall, the dust and paper whirling in the breeze.

The dining room in East Hall was operated on a cooperative plan, with the cost of food prorated, averaging two dollars a week. (No wonder there were complaints about the fare.) Since Trevor had volunteered as a cook, he got his meals free. He had assumed that in comparison with his experience in the logging camp, cooking for students would be easy; but he found they ate just as much as the loggers did and their table manners were just as rough.

The first and most important rule for a boarder to learn, he discovered, was to be on time for meals, and "not to stub his toe answering the call." The first man at the table got the biggest piece of meat, and there were no seconds.

With his domestic affairs in order, the young man could hardly wait to become a student. Because he had not attended the high school in Olympia and the private school conducted in Peterborough by the Oxford graduate had not used the traditional system of marking, Trevor had no record of his achievements. To take the place of this record, he had to write a series of tests in practically all high school subjects. Having passed these satisfactorily, he was allowed to enter the University as a "conditioned" freshman. Mathematics and Latin had to be made up during the year. He rushed through the mathematics with ease; his practice of covering reams of wrapping paper in the hardware store with geometry theorems and algebra problems made it almost like a game. Latin was made easy through the translation of Livy's *History* that he had made during the long winter evenings. Kincaid said:

When I came to the University the staff consisted of eight instructors, including President Gatch, who taught some classes. J. M. Taylor and Lieutenant J. E. Hayden taught Mathematics (Hayden was also Commandant of Cadets); Lois Hansee taught English; Charles Hill taught Science. The names of the teachers of languages and music have escaped my memory.

The enrollment was between 250 and 275, including the janitors, the elementary pupils, and the "special" students. All told, only fifteen degrees had been conferred during the first thirty-three years of the University's life. The first degree was granted in 1876 to Miss Clara McCarty.

Kincaid was dismayed to find he was expected to join the Cadet Corps and to buy a uniform that cost fifteen dollars. He had no intention of doing this. He did not have the fifteen dollars and he did not approve of students shouldering guns and preparing for war. When he was told that military training gave a man the manly bearing and upright posture so necessary for a student, he laughed and said his long hikes and his field trips had given him the exercise he needed, and he could take care of the manly posture. He was excused from the Cadet Corps.

Probably the worst disillusionment in the high purpose of University students came to the young idealist when, a few days after school opened, Miss Hansee asked the freshmen to write a 500-word theme on a subject of their own choosing. Most of them had never written a 100-word letter; how could they write 500 words on any subject? Most of the freshmen solved their dilemma by hiring the learned seniors to write their essays, paying them fifty cents for doing so. "Some of them made quite a stake,"

Trevor concluded. He wrote his paper on "Collecting Insects in the Vicinity of Olympia."

Another disappointment came to him when he learned that Professor Johnson would not teach the class in zoology during the coming school year. For a couple of years Johnson had suffered from a rheumatoid arthritis condition, which had recently become so painful that the doctor suggested he go east to consult specialists. Perhaps mud baths, mineral waters, or heat treatments might be beneficial.

In the short time Kincaid had known Professor Johnson, he had developed a deep respect and admiration for him, and he had looked forward to association with him. He knew too that in a number of ways their backgrounds were alike. Both had a vast curiosity about the natural world and could have said with Charles Darwin, "I would like to know everything about every sort of plant and animal on earth."

Both loved to follow a stream or climb a mountain, noting the minutest living thing along the way. Both loved the smell of the rain and the caress of the wind. Both enjoyed the simple pleasures of life and had a deep and abiding faith in their fellow men.

In other ways, too, the two men's lives were parallel. After the close of the Civil War, Johnson had received a law degree, but he never practiced, because about the time of his graduation he had heard the famous Louis Agassiz deliver a lecture on natural science. With that introduction to the field of biology, Johnson knew he had found his life work. He resolved to leave Vermont and go to Oregon, where he could live in God's beautiful out-of-doors, where the woods and the mountains beckoned and where the animals were still free and wild.

The entire faculty of the University of Washington in 1894. Orson Bennett Johnson (far right) was the only instructor in the science department.

In Oregon, Johnson became a surveyor for the pro-
jected Northern Pacific Railroad. Between driving
stakes in the proposed roadway, he gathered hundreds of plants and animals, as Kincaid did later, and
supplemented his surveyor's salary by selling plant
and shell collections to persons who were interested
in that popular hobby.

In 1882 Johnson was offered the professorship in
science in the University of Washington; he had
reached the pinnacle of his ambition. He became
such a successful teacher and had such a dynamic
personality that in a few months he ranked just below the President in the University hierarchy and
was receiving a salary of $1,800 per year.

Johnson was the only instructor in the science department, and the teaching load he was called upon
to carry was more than any human being could possibly bear. According to the catalog of 1892, he was
scheduled to teach all the courses in botany, zoology,
mineralogy, geology, chemistry, and physics. (Fortunately, many of them existed only on paper.) On a
brief visit to Seattle, Dr. Charles Eliot, President of
Harvard University, said of Johnson's workload: "He
occupies not a chair but a settee."

To take charge of Johnson's classes during his sick
leave, Charles Hill, a man still in his early thirties, a
graduate of the University of Michigan with a master's degree in zoology, had been brought to the University.

Hill was not so deeply interested in natural history
as Johnson had been, and he had little time or inclina-
tion for field work. He was a morphologist, who had
studied the form, structure, and classification of animals. Naturally he patterned his invertebrate
zoology course after a class he had taken in Michigan

in which the students first studied the simple forms of life, such as the protozoans and the sponges, then proceeded to the more complex starfish, barnacles, and snails.

Under Charles Hill, Trevor was introduced to the systematic study of zoology, saying: "It was exactly the course I needed to round out my wide but rather haphazard knowledge of the animal world and it gave me a clear picture of evolution."

Although Kincaid had read Darwin's *Origin of Species* in the Humboldt Series of Classics, he knew little about the phyla under which animals were grouped and the relationships between them. Kincaid was born between two eras—that in which most men still believed in a literal interpretation of the first chapter of Genesis, and the modern age in which they believed in a gradual evolution of life on earth by natural processes over millions of years. Everything Kincaid had observed in his own ramblings and reading had confirmed the latter belief. And Professor Hill's course reinforced and strengthened that conviction. From the beginning there was a splendid rapport between Hill and Kincaid, and in the absence of Professor Johnson, Hill became the greatest influence in Trevor's early college days.

The entire science department was housed in one room on the second floor of the main building. A narrow alcove, 12' × 15', on one side of the room served as the chemistry laboratory. Two long tables on the other side constituted the biology department, and one wall was allotted to the physics department. With a dozen or more chairs placed in the center of the room, it was transformed into a lecture hall. The one professor scuttled back and forth to serve all three departments.

Also on the second floor was an assembly room in which chapel services were conducted each morning. Close by was a library nook about the size of a closet. The books were government documents and discarded novels donated by townspeople. The library was growing, however, for according to the catalog of 1888, an allotment of $600 was made for its operation.

Despite the meagerness of the quarters and the equipment of the zoology department, Kincaid became so enthralled with studying the form and structure of invertebrate animals under Charles Hill that he sat in the small, ill-lighted laboratory from morning until night, peering through an outmoded microscope. Working out the anatomy of an earthworm, a barnacle, or a frog, and classifying the animal into its proper family, genus, and species was like solving a complex mathematical problem, each form fitting properly into its evolutionary niche. If Hill had not driven him from the room at midnight, Trevor would, no doubt, have spent the night there, unconscious of the passing of time. Certainly it was in this crowded room that Kincaid began to form a coherent view of the creation of life in this planet.

The eight students in Professor Hill's invertebrate zoology class took turns reading the assignment from a translation of a German text, the personal property of Hill. In conducting his class, Hill employed an effective psychological technique: he quizzed the students on the assignment; then at the end of the period, looking each one straight in the eye, he entered a grade in his class book. The fear of that stare and of seeing a zero being recorded for the day's work compelled the students to study diligently.

Just as Johnson had been overburdened with

classes, Hill was expected to handle far more courses than one man could manage. He was a most conscientious teacher, but when a course in pharmaceutical botany was thrust upon him, he nearly rebelled. An important part of the course would be the making of an herbarium of the local plants, especially those which had medicinal properties. He swore he could not add another course to his already heavy schedule.

Young Kincaid, who realized the extra burden this course would be on Hill's time, offered to check the students' notebooks. When Hill learned that the industrious young student had been collecting plants and animals for years and sending them to scientists in all parts of the country, he gladly turned over this onerous duty to him. Trevor checked the herbaria so meticulously that the professor was soon giving him other duties around the department, sending him to vacant lots to collect frogs and to the seashore for starfish and snails for class use. Collecting was sheer pleasure to Kincaid; Charles Hill had found a first-class helper.

In spite of Trevor's economy and careful fingering of every nickel before he let it slip through his hands, the ten-dollar gold piece was almost gone. He looked everywhere for a job, but the storekeepers needed no helpers. No newspaper routes were available; it was winter and no lawns needed mowing, and the furnaces were already supplied with stokers.

He caressed the silver dollar in his back pocket and wondered if the time had come for him to return to Olympia. He could not bear to think of that possibility, for he realized that small and struggling though the University was, it offered him far greater inspira-

tion than anything in Olympia could. He was in good
health and was not afraid of the hardest work. He was
willing to try anything, but he did not know where
to turn for employment.

One evening when he was sitting in his ugly dormitory room, literally counting his pennies, he heard
the tapping of a cane far down the hall. The door
opened and in hobbled Professor Johnson, who had
just heard of Kincaid's predicament from members
of the Young Naturalists' Society. So, the night before
leaving for the East for treatment, he came to see
Trevor, the brilliant student about whom everyone
was talking.

For a moment Johnson looked about the forlorn
little room with the makeshift bed and packing-box
chair. Then without a word he dropped a twenty-
dollar gold piece on the table trunk, turned hurriedly, and was out of the room. Kincaid was so
touched by Professor Johnson's generosity that he
wrote him a note saying he hoped some day to be as
fine a scientist and as great an inspiration to young
men as he (Johnson) was.

Neither the mud baths nor the Eastern doctors
could help Johnson's arthritis, so when he returned
to Seattle, he was in a wheel chair. Soon Johnson was
relieved of his University teaching, but Trevor remained his disciple until his death many years later.

He knew that Johnson would soon tire of classifying and mounting local materials over and over
again, so Kincaid rarely went on a field trip or visited
a far country without bringing a duplicate collection
to his old mentor. When Johnson opened a box from
Trevor, he would say, "Trevor, you are the finest and
most loyal friend a man could have."

Johnson died in March, 1917. In spite of his unremitting work and his large collections, he had published almost nothing. Kincaid believed this
hesitancy stemmed largely from inadequate library
facilities, for he had no way of verifying his own classifications, and rather than run the risk of an incor-
rect listing, he did not attempt to publish his findings.

When his collections were deposited in the University Museum after his death, they contained 10,000
butterflies, skippers, and moths and 12,000 beetles—
certainly the most complete set of insects in the
Northwest. Dr. Melville Hatch, as late as 1960, reported that 40 years after Johnson's death, the immense collection was still in excellent condition with
at least 90 percent of it as useful then as when it was
made.

Instead of encouraging students to make their own
collections, Johnson had suggested they add their
material to his. Although Johnson often spoke of his
belief in evolution, his collections were made up almost exclusively of two specimens of an animal, a
male and a female, showing none of the variations
that occur in the long evolutionary development of
a species. Yet Kincaid says there is no question that
to Orson Bennett Johnson belongs the honor of giving the first impetus to research on the University of
Washington campus.

Trevor's financial plight soon became known to
the Young Naturalists. When Johnson's twenty dollars were down to fifty cents, Edmond Meany, a
member of the group and for many years one of
Kincaid's most loyal friends, came to tell him that
Charles Denny, son of one of the founders of Seattle
and also a member of the Society, wished him to
make his home with them for the rest of the year.

A few days later Trevor arrived at the back door of the Denny home, trundling his trunk and his boxes of insects in a cart. He expected he would be asked to care for the furnace and do other chores around the house and eat with the servants. Instead of showing him a room in the basement, Mrs. Denny ushered him into a large bright room on the second floor, gave him a key to the front door, and insisted he eat his meals with the family. When he asked what his duties would be, she said there would be none. Two long-time servants took care of the house, and an elderly gardener tended the yard.

When Trevor offered to work on Saturdays at the Denny clay works, Mr. Denny made it clear he could spend his Saturdays to better advantage working on his scientific projects. This he did by accompanying Brooks Randolph almost every weekend on a collecting expedition into Puget Sound.

Randolph was a bailiff in the United States District Court in Seattle, but his hobby was collecting shells. His father, a former tugboat captain on the Skagit River, had recently given his son a small boat, the *Maud*. The minute the week's work was done, Randolph and Kincaid, who had taken a great liking to one another, set off on a dredging trip into Puget Sound. Once outside the city, they nosed the *Maud* up to a log-strewn beach and gathered enough driftwood to fill the stokehole; then they looked for a dock where they could take on water for the boiler. Kincaid made a four-foot net of bunting and by trailing it astern was able to haul in a myriad of tiny sea creatures.

As an aid to collecting larger animals, the young marine scientists installed a dredge on the back of the boat, which could be drawn onto the deck by a windlass operated by "two cranks." When Trevor saw a starfish with its hundreds of tube feet, a sea urchin covered with long sharp spines, a crab trying to manage its ten legs, or an octopus with its writhing arms brought up in the dredge, he was filled with wonder at the beauty and variety of life on the seashore, and he had a feeling of reverence for the overall plan and purpose of life.

When it became too dark to dredge, "the two cranks" dropped anchor in a protected cove and fried their bacon and eggs on a shovel in the fire box; they boiled their coffee in an empty tomato can and steamed their clams by dropping them into the coals. Their hunger appeased, they stretched out on the deck and slept until the sun awakened them. What matter the mattresses were filled with pine needles and the coffee pot a tin can? Trevor was in heaven.

Many things besides classes, the laboratory, and even the *Maud* stimulated Trevor Kincaid during his first year at the University. The Dennys' generosity allowed him to forget the barren dormitory room. He still had his insurance dollar in his back pocket. He had carved a niche for himself in the zoology department, and he was taking part in University activities.

Two literary societies with very impressive names —the Altheonians and the Philomatheans—played an important role in University life at the time. Kincaid joined the Philomatheans and plunged into their programs with the same vigor with which he had participated in Mr. Balleau's study group in Olympia. He read short reports on the animals dredged up on the *Maud,* took part in debates, gave book reviews and poetry readings. In fact, he appeared on the program at every opportunity, for he felt that training in public speaking was very necessary to the poise and dignity of a man.

But without question it was the Young Naturalists' Society that gave Kincaid a group of friends and a viewpoint far broader than he had had before and that no University course could have provided. This group had been organized in 1879 in the home of Brooks Randolph by half a dozen young men 18 or 20 years of age with broad tastes and high hopes of learning about the plants and animals of the Northwest. In fact, the young men were such indefatigable collectors that their material furnished the first endemic study of natural history in Washington.

The members of the group were amateurs, men both in the University and the city of Seattle, but the organization became so highly respected by University Presidents that the Regents offered them a 25-year lease on a piece of land 56 X 30 feet on the campus for a building at a rental of a dollar per year. During the twenty years of its life, almost ninety persons were elected to membership in the Young Naturalists' group. The most loyal members through the years were: Charles A. Denny, taxidermist and Seattle capitalist; F. Brooks Randolph, conchologist and bailiff; Edward Chilberg, conchologist, philanthropist, and banker; E. C. Cheasty, businessman; Lawrence J. Colman, capitalist and philanthropist; Orson Bennett Johnson, professor of science; James F. McElroy, attorney; Edmond Meany, state legislator; Charles W. Piper, professor of botany at Washington State College. Later members were Adam Hubbard, Sr.; Charles Hill; Stephen B. White; Henry Landes; David Starr Jordan; and Trevor Kincaid. With tremendous eagerness and much oratory the members presented essays a page or two long on different kinds of animals. One of the most exciting meetings was a debate, "Resolved that the Colorado Potato Bug is an Injury to Mankind." The negative side won.

The Young Naturalists also built up a library of magazines far superior to that in the general University library. When Trevor Kincaid arrived in Seattle in 1894, he found an array of magazines on the shelves such as he had never seen before: *Scientific American, American Naturalist, Erythea, Torrey's Botanical Club Bulletin, Popular Scientific Monthly, The Auk, Oregon Naturalist, Botanical Gazette, Canadian Entomologist, Entomological News,* and *The Nautilus.* With this wealth of reading matter at hand he could not decide what to read first.

Eventually the Society's library and collections of scientific materials became so large that Henry Havelock was appointed librarian and curator. Unfortunately, he did not follow the basic dictum for all scientific work, "Leave nothing to memory." He kept the data in his head instead of on labels, which eventually made the collection worthless.

With the coming of Kincaid to the University, the Young Naturalists' Society took on new life. At his suggestion the members began active correspondence and exchange of specimens with biologists in all parts of the country and won national acclaim from men interested in the fauna and flora of the Northwest. During the summers of 1894, 1895, and 1896, Kincaid joined the Young Naturalists on dredging expeditions into Puget Sound, which were partially financed by the University. E. C. Sparks, a student of David Starr Jordan of Stanford, published an annotated list of Puget Sound fishes as a result of the work done on these trips, the first research done by the zoology department.

The Young Naturalists' interest in their society, however, began to wane after 1896. Several attempts to recruit new members were harbingers of the end. Kincaid explained this by saying that the Young Naturalists had become old naturalists. Business and professional interests had supplanted their youthful hobbies, and undoubtedly Professor Johnson's illness had robbed it of its most dominant spirit.

The removal of the University from its downtown location to the shores of Lake Washington in 1895 made it necessary for the Society to move or disband. They chose the latter course. It was quite possible, too, Kincaid believed, that the Young Naturalists had come to be considered trespassers on the campus, for they had often stolen the spotlight from the University itself.

Although the Young Naturalists were no more, they had fostered and kept alive the scientific spirit in the Northwest, and through their efforts the University museum and the Library had become solidly established. Above all, they had brought recognition to themselves and fame to the University.

A dramatic leap forward for the University was being considered at this time. Ever since 1889, when Washington had attained statehood, it had been realized that the "campus on the knoll" was too small and the location highly unsuitable for a University, surrounded as it was by saloons, bawdy theaters, and real estate offices. Edmond Meany, an 1885 graduate of the University and a legislator, was appointed chairman of a committee to look for a new site. A number of locations had been suggested, but Meany maintained that the shore of Lake Washington, near the junction of Lake Washington and Lake Union with its superb view of Mount Rainier and the great expanse of water, was the ideal location. Certainly an argument in its favor was that already the area was part of designated school lands.

In an impassioned plea before the influential lumbermen in the legislature, Meany pointed out the advantage of this location for what he termed an "arboretum" for the study of economic forestry. Despite his eloquence, one legislator was unconvinced. Shortly before the question was to come to a vote, the "Doubting Thomas" went to Meany and whispered confidentially, "Meany, I believe in higher education and I want to support your bill, but tell me before I vote, 'What the hell is an arboretum?' " Whether or not that was the deciding argument, the doubtful member voted "aye" and the Legislator designated the beautiful 582-acre tract on Lake Washington as the new campus.

Owing to delays in financing and the inability of the Regents to sell the old campus for an acceptable price (in the long run a fortunate thing), two and a half years elapsed before a decision was made on the location of the University building.

The ground was cleared, and on July 4, 1894, the cornerstone for Denny Hall was laid with fitting ceremonies. In planning for the science department, President Gatch called Charles Hill into conference to discuss faculty needs. Hill asked for two new professors, one in chemistry and one in physics, and an assistant for each instructor.

Gatch exploded. "Good heavens, man, with three professors in science, we will be top-heavy with scientists. And what do they need assistants for? Surely an instructor can wash his own bottles." Gatch assured Hill, however, that he would ask for the men, although he had little hope for the appointments.

Charles Hill's choice for his own assistant was Trevor Kincaid. The day came when the Regents would decide whether bottle-washers were necessary. Trevor walked around in a daze all day. Would they appoint him, a mere freshman, to such an exalted position? The next morning, as he was hurrying across the campus for an eight o'clock class, he met Lieutenant Hayden. As a passing greeting, Hayden hailed Kincaid, "My old man tells me they took you in out of the rain last night."

"Hurrah," shouted Kincaid in response. He was an assistant in the University at the princely salary of $25 a month. To him it was princely indeed. He was on the first rung of the academic ladder and from that date on, Trevor Kincaid's life was in important measure that of the zoology department and of the University of Washington.

On the last day of classes on the old campus, the students joined in a most unscholarly ceremony. They assembled almost to a man in front of the Old Main Building, carrying boxes, logs, anything combustible, and built a pyre into which they threw lighted torches. When the fire was raging, the students filed past the pyre chanting and throwing their books into the flaming mass. Kincaid refused to participate in the orgy. To him books were far too precious to be wantonly destroyed. In his *Autobiography* he stated that fortunately this was the last year of this performance. The University Book Store was soon opened in a small room in Denny Hall, and used books were sold at a discount for the next year's students.

With the assurance that Kincaid would be his assistant on the new campus, Professor Hill gave him more and more duties around the zoology department. A project he particularly enjoyed was making plaster models for Hill's course in comparative anatomy of vertebrates. When finished, the models gave a graphic picture of the changes that had taken place in the skulls of frogs, fishes, cats, horses, and man during millions of years of evolution. As the young scientist studied these animals, he wished the Methodist minister in Peterborough could see the proofs of evolution they presented. It was a perfect example of adaptation and the survival of the fittest. Another assignment the young assistant enjoyed was unpacking and assembling equipment for the new zoology department. Among them were a Naples bath, a microtome, and compound and dissecting microscopes, aids to scientific study Kincaid did not know existed.

One morning the new bottle-washer was so engrossed in inspecting these aids to scientific progress that he did not notice a tall, handsome stranger walk into the room. "I'm looking for Professor Hill. Is he about?" the visitor asked. When he learned that Hill was out of town for a few days, the stranger, who introduced himself as David Starr Jordan, President of Stanford University, sat down on a packing box and talked to the bright-eyed, cheerful young student for several hours about the undreamed possibilities that high-powered microscopes and other scientific instruments opened up to scientists.

In speaking of the encounter later, Kincaid said, "I must have made a favorable impression upon him, for during the next twenty years Jordan was my friend, opening up many fine opportunities to me, even offering me a teaching position at Stanford."

The new University campus opened its doors on September 5, 1895. In contrast to the simple colonial building on the knoll with its four Ionic columns, Denny Hall, built of limestone in French Renaissance style with impressive stone steps, turrets, and many-windowed circular classrooms seemed little less than palatial to Trevor Kincaid and other students.

Many Seattleites had believed that the removal of the University from its downtown location to the shore of Lake Washington, a distance of five miles, would isolate the young school beyond the reach of most townspeople. The installation of streetcars in 1889 and the construction of a narrow wooden bridge across Lake Union at Fremont Street in 1892 lessened the distance between the two points, however, and hastened the acceptance of the new campus in the public mind.

The area around the new campus developed rapidly and soon became known as the University District. Grocery stores, restaurants, and a shoe-repairing shop sprang up. A number of large houses were built for the faculty and sprawling boarding houses for students. Mail for the University was brought from downtown by carrier, while students and residents collected their mail at a small grocery store run by an elderly couple in the Fremont District.

Previously there had been little development north of the campus. Some of the tall trees were still standing, but it was mostly stump land traversed by ancient logging trails. Kincaid said that a dirt road, almost impassable in winter, ran from the north edge of the campus to Green Lake. Anyone brave enough to travel that road at night of necessity carried a lantern and wore rubber boots.

Mr. and Mrs. Denny, who had become almost like second parents to Trevor, asked him to continue to live with them, even suggesting they adopt him as their son, but much as he had enjoyed their hospitality and appreciated their deep concern for him, he refused, for regardless of his father's rejection of his family responsibilities, he was fiercely loyal to him and parental ties. Moreover, he realized he could save two precious hours each day if he roomed near the campus.

He had intended to live in a boarding house, but Mrs. Kincaid's plan to care for her son's motherless children in New York did not work out satisfactorily, so she and her daughters returned to Olympia after a few months. Since Dr. Kincaid did not feel disposed to care for them, there was nothing for Trevor to do but to bring them to Seattle to live with him. To accommodate them, he rented a house not far from the campus for seven dollars a month and supported them all on his bottle-washer's salary.

The University catalog of 1895–96 stated that Denny Hall, with 20,000 square feet of floor space, could adequately serve a student body of 600 to 700 for years to come. Several new members were added to the faculty and, despite the raising of the entrance requirements, enrollment increased considerably. The elementary school, which until this time had been a part of the University, was abolished, but many high school students and subfreshmen with no educational requirements specified were still being enrolled.

On opening day, although the carpenters were still busy with saws and hammers, hanging doors and laying floors, Charles Hill and Trevor Kincaid were very proud of the semi-circular classrooms and laboratories assigned to the zoology department on the first floor and in the basement of Denny Hall. The laboratories were equipped to serve 72 students, an enrollment beyond Hill's wildest dreams.

Even with the new professors of chemistry and physics, Professor Hill's teaching load was very heavy. In addition to general zoology, embryology, anatomy, and physiology, he was asked to take on a subfreshman class in general biology. How could he teach an extra class? Having no one else to turn to, he asked Trevor Kincaid to take charge of the class. Consequently, Kincaid, who had just finished the freshman class himself, taught the incoming freshmen.

One day while proctoring an examination, Kincaid caught a student copying the answers from the textbook. At the end of the class period, the boy, realizing his dishonesty had been discovered, walked to Kincaid's desk and asked somewhat defiantly, "Well, what are you going to do with me?" Kincaid picked up the paper, tore it in two, and dropped the pieces into the wastebasket, saying, "Give you a great big zero for the course." Some years later, during the annual visit of the Board of Regents to the University, Kincaid was not a little surprised to find that the erstwhile cheating student had become a president of a bank and also President of the Board of Regents.

Determined to make the first class he had ever taught interesting, Kincaid often got up at five o'clock and walked to Ballard Beach (later called Golden Gardens) to gather material for demonstration purposes. One morning the class assembled at ten o'clock but the teacher did not appear. The students decided he had forgotten all about them. Just as they were leaving the classroom, Kincaid appeared wearing but one shoe and struggling with a bucket in which were a dozen or more wriggling, squirming crabs as intent on getting out of the container as he was in keeping them in.

Out of breath, the professor explained between bursts of laughter that he had wanted to show how crabs use their ten feet in walking—a remarkable example of coordination. In pulling a big fellow out of the mud, he had stepped into a hole and his shoe came off. He knew he was late for class, and having trouble with the crabs, he left his shoe behind. "But here I am," he announced gaily. "I'll dispose of the crabs. And, incidentally, how about a crab feed after class?"

As might have been anticipated, removal of the still struggling University from one location to another posed innumerable difficulties for the administrative officers. Many of the problems stemmed from the Board of Regents. Each newly elected Governor appointed a new Board of Regents, who took it upon themselves to administer the University down to the minutest detail. They hired and fired teachers without consulting the President, and made policies contrary to his wishes. They even tried to dictate the content of the courses and influence the expenditure of departmental funds. In fact, the President was treated more like a foreman than an executive.

Dr. Gatch, who had been President for several years, foreseeing the difficulties that lay ahead, resigned a few weeks after the opening of the new campus. A younger man would be better able to cope with the greatly expanded University, he said. In a final lecture to the students, he admonished:

Young men, young women, what can you do this coming year that will be of such incredible benefit in the life struggle before you as to devote your time and energies to the acquisition of knowledge and mental discipline and be a well spring of joy in all the years of your life? Do not allow trifling obstacles and allurements of your youthful pleasures and sports to turn you aside from your purpose to secure an education.

With the resignation of President Gatch, Dr. Mark Harrington was appointed to the Presidency. Years later Kincaid said that Harrington might well have been the most highly educated man ever to preside over the destinies of the University. In addition to having been Chief of the Weather Bureau in Washington and professor of astronomy at the University of Michigan, he spoke German and French fluently and could teach Latin and Greek. He also had a broad knowledge of zoology, as Kincaid learned one morning when he was working over a microscope on a paper dealing with a group of minute moth flies, the *Psychodides.*

The President walked into the laboratory and looked over the shoulder of the young instructor a second. Finally he inquired, "What characters are you using to separate the species"?

Kincaid was surprised, for he did not know that there were more than three persons in the state of Washington who could have asked that question. (A character, according to the dictionary, is a trait, function, or substance of an organism resulting from a gene, a hereditary characteristic.)

From the beginning, Harrington was hampered by what he called the immaturity of the University, the lack of funds to operate the school, the bickering and cliques within the faculty. The difficulties with the Regents began when Harrington recommended that the subfreshman courses be discontinued, saying, "The fundamental spirit of secondary education is opposed to that of a University which is one of free untrammeled inquiry. No great University has ever been built up with a secondary attachment."

He also believed the Schools of Music and Art should be dropped, because they did not meet the standards of a University requiring a liberal education for a degree, and that degrees in physical education should not be granted unless the candidate met regular scholastic requirements. The Regents completely ignored his suggestions.

In a further attempt to bring the quality of instruction at the University up to par with that of universities in older states, Harrington hired faculty members from all sections of the country. These new appointments changed the character of the school in many ways and helped rid it of some of its strictly local features.

Formerly Dr. Gatch had been the only man on the faculty with a Ph.D. degree; six of the fifteen brought in by Harrington to teach collegiate subjects had doctor's degrees and seven held master's degrees either in science or in arts.

Naturally, the importation of outsiders made the pioneer group uneasy, for the newcomers introduced points of view that the "Westerners" could not always accept. Inevitably, jealousy arose between the "home town boys" and the "foreigners." Several of the older group, notably Edmond Meany, realized that if they were to compete with the more widely trained men, they would have to seek more education. Kincaid's position seemed secure because, although still an undergraduate, his wide exchange of scientific materials and his research put him in a class by himself.

When Harrington came to the University, he gave promise of being a man of firm convictions and a fighter for what he believed the school needed, but under the pressures of financial problems, politics and personal affairs, he failed to develop the qualities of leadership expected of him.

He lost much of his influence in the state in 1896 when the Populists came into power in Washington and the legislature was filled with men who were critical of the city, and everything it implied, including the University and its President, particularly his lack of political participation and his $5,000 salary. A severe blow to Harrington's personal pride occurred when he fell over a cow in the dark. The campus was still a forest of tree stumps among which wandered a great many cows. His encounter with the cow was widely publicized, much to his embarrassment, and may well have been the last straw in his disillusionment with the University of Washington. In any case, he resigned soon afterwards. To prove, perhaps, that he took no offense at the Regents' suggestion that he resign, he gave several hundred books from his private collection to the University, a gift that greatly improved the size and quality of the library.

With Harrington's departure, the Regents adopted a policy that a man of moderate talents but one faithful and deserving was safer in the long run than a brilliant scholar like Harrington. With this in mind, William Edwards, a professor of physics, was appointed President. Both Edwards and his successor, Charles Reeves, a German teacher, resigned after holding office less than a year.

During this time a serious slump set in, one that crippled the University for several years. Kincaid called it "a mimic warfare of politics and religion." For example, it was rumored that certain members of the faculty were to be dismissed, including a

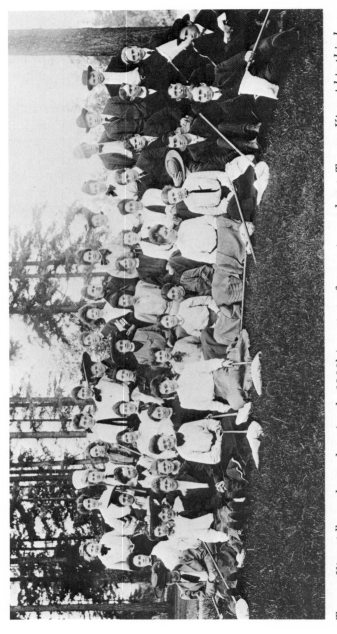

Trevor Kincaid's zoology class (early 1900's) resting after an insect hunt. Trevor Kincaid is third from the right in the front row.

retired Presbyterian minister, Edward J. Hamilton, who taught philosophy classes that were required of all students preparing to teach. Hamilton's knowledge of philosophy was limited to the fundamentalist theory of the creation of the earth as recorded in the first chapter of Genesis. In his lectures he went to great pains to prove the theory of evolution to be the work of the devil.

This narrow point of view irritated Kincaid and other members of the faculty who had some knowledge of the great thinkers of the past. President Edwards contended that Hamilton's philosophy belonged in a theological seminary, not in a state university. Hamilton retaliated by saying he was being persecuted and that Edwards was an atheist.

When Dr. Thaddeus Bolton was appointed to the Chair of Philosophy and Education, he at once took charge of the courses required of teachers himself, while Hamilton's became elective, which left him practically without students.

Kincaid, who was now a sophomore, was determined to remain outside these controversies; he took refuge in his studies, his laboratory, and his books by continuing his investigation of the moth fly. Little was known of these obscure little creatures, and none had previously been described from the Northwest. The fly was so small it could not be studied with the microscope formerly used in the Department. But by using a compound microscope, included in the new equipment, Kincaid made slide mounts of every part of the fly's anatomy.

During the same year he wrote a second paper on the moth flies, and the next year made a study of a milliped, a species of *Polynexus* that lives under the bark of trees. These papers, the first to come from the fertile brain and facile pen of Trevor Kincaid, were

highly technical and therefore interesting only to
entomologists. They were published in the *Entomological News* in Philadelphia and brought him recognition not only on his own campus but also abroad.
No poet was ever prouder of seeing his verses in
print than was Kincaid when he read his first papers
in a scientific journal.

Even in those early days, Kincaid's determination
to remain outside political disputes stirred up severe
criticism. His more argumentative colleagues said he
did not have the courage to stand up for his beliefs.
In spite of this criticism, through more than 50 years
on the campus he continued to follow this policy.
Through his geniality, his quiet persuasion, and his
solid scholarship, he saw the fulfillment of most of the
things in which he believed—the education of young
people, service to the state, the dissemination of information about the plants and animals of the region,
and the maintenance of his own personal independence. Perhaps it was the disputes within the young
University that gave him a lasting indifference to
political and social organizations.

To get away from the unpleasant conditions at the
University, Charles Hill asked for a leave of absence
to complete his work for a medical degree at Northwestern University. Homer Redfield Foster, who
came to take his place, was a competent botanist, but
he had practically no training in zoology. When he
learned that he was expected to teach a course in
comparative anatomy of vertebrate animals, he was
dismayed. In his predicament, he begged Kincaid to
teach the course. Immediately the young undergraduate recalled the models he had made for Hill's
anatomy class; he felt sure he could use them to advantage in his own class.

The result was a happy exchange, Kincaid teaching the anatomy course and Foster the botany course. Foster's reluctance to handle the zoology course left Kincaid the virtual head of the zoology department. Kincaid was no older than many of his students, so the boys and their favorite teacher often went on field trips to the mountains, forests, or seashore. On these outings Kincaid's remarkable memory, his keen powers of observation, his good humor, and his teaching methods of leading from the known to the unknown and drawing conclusions only after long, close observation made a deep impression on the young students. His persistence in demanding proof of a statement, that ever-present "why," put the boys on their mettle.

CHAPTER 4

Two Trips
to Alaska

BY 1897 TREVOR KINCAID'S reputation as a scientist
had spread beyond the boundaries of the University
of Washington. In the summer of his twenty-third
year he was invited to go to Alaska, the first of many
scientific expeditions which, through the years, took
him to far places of the earth. The immediate object
of the journey was to investigate the fur seals that
summered on the Pribilof Islands, treeless bits of volcanic land thrust up far out in the Bering Sea.

For untold ages the great, awkward seals, whose
coats were highly prized by women for their warmth
and beauty, had arrived on the Pribilof Islands, about
two hundred miles off the Alaska coast, each spring
to bear and rear their young. Some ancient instinct
seemed to draw thousands of fur seals from the eastern Pacific to a few square miles of bare rock and
crumbling soil bordering these islands.

As soon as the young were able to undertake the
long journey in the late summer, they left the Pribilof Islands and moved down the Pacific Coast to the
latitude of the Hawaiian Islands, where they spent
the winter disporting themselves on the warm tropical beaches.

During these migrations both to and from the
North the seals were being slaughtered in great num-

bers by pelagic sealers based in Canada. This practice had become so widespread that ill feeling had arisen among the several countries involved in the sealing industry, and it was feared some incident might lead to war. More serious than the international feeling, however, was the very real danger that the seals might become extinct.

In order to settle the matter of promiscuous slaughtering, Grover Cleveland, President of the United States, called an international conference in 1897. David Starr Jordan was asked to go to the Pribilofs with a group of scientists to study the problem. His American assistants were Dr. F. A. Lucas and Dr. Leonard Stjener of the National Museum. The British government sent Dr. D'Arcy Thompson and Dr. Barrett Hamilton. Canada's representative was Dr. James Macoun. Because Russia had a herd of seals on the Commander Islands and Japan had a herd on the Bonin Islands, they were asked to participate in the discussions.

To carry out the details of the three-month program, Dr. Jordan selected a group of students from Stanford. When at the last minute one of them became ill, he asked Trevor Kincaid to take his place. Trevor's direct and friendly manner charmed everyone in the party.

Jordan's party traveled as far as Sitka on a commercial steamer. Here Kincaid saw for the first time the beautiful scenery of the Inside Passage to Alaska with its mountains and glaciers just beyond the shores. By changing the pronouns, it could have been said of Trevor Kincaid, as Browning said in "My Last Duchess," "She liked whate'er she looked on, and her looks went everywhere."

From Sitka, the party traveled aboard the *Alba-*

tross, the United States Fish Commission boat, equipped as a floating laboratory. The *Albatross* stopped at several of the Aleutian Islands. Regardless of wind or rain or storm, Kincaid was busy with net and cyanide bottle at each stop. At Dutch Harbor the party transferred to a revenue cutter bound for the Pribilofs. The fog was so thick that the ship's captain was forced to navigate by compass and dead reckoning.

As the ship was moving through one particularly dense fog bank, a sudden weird cry was heard close by as if thousands of animals were terrorized. "What could have caused it?," asked Kincaid.

The skipper believed that herds of sea lions had been lying on the reefs and the sound of the approaching ship had frightened them and caused them to dive into the water. Had it not been for the cries of the sea lions, the ship might have crashed onto the reef. Perpetual rains, sunless skies, and dense fogs were the spectres that haunted a navigator in the Bering Sea, the captain explained, and ships had been known to hover for weeks trying to find a safe passage into the open ocean.

After a brief stop on St. George's Island, the cutter headed for St. Paul's Island, approximately forty miles away, the headquarters of the sealing industry. The two islands comprised the Pribilof group. Since there was no harbor on St. Paul's, the scientists were rowed ashore by Aleuts in large boats made of sealion skins.

The approach to the village was bleak. As he walked up the narrow, rutted street, Kincaid saw that it consisted only of the unpainted business office of the sealing company, a store, a schoolhouse, sheds for drying the sealskins for shipment, and rows of low almost windowless cabins where the workers lived. Even the clothes of the women who gathered on the shore to greet the newcomers were dark and unadorned, their heads swathed in black scarves, their feet shod in clumsy rubber boots. The only spot of color in the village was the Russian Orthodox Church with its bright blue turrets and onion-shaped dome set high upon a hill. Just beyond the village was the tundra, the vast marshy plain that covers much of Alaska.

The men of the expedition were housed in an abandoned billiard hall with beds arranged along the walls. A few chairs and a couple of shelves comprised the furnishings. The dining room was equipped with long, bare tables. A large coal stove provided heat.

As a first step in studying the seals, Dr. Jordan set the young students to branding the animals with an electric torch. The quarreling, lumbering males objected violently to this indignity. They attacked their tormentors and drove them from their harems, jealously guarding the cows and their young.

The students also objected to this unpleasant work. Kincaid did not like it either, but he knew the participation in the study gave him a wonderful opportunity, so accepting the unpleasant things with the good, he quickly adapted himself to his new duties. The next job assigned the young men was building a fence around a lagoon where they could observe the behavior of the individual seals. While the students were building the fence, Dr. Jordan went to St. George's Island on a business trip, so the students declared a holiday from their drudgery.

Since arriving on the island, Kincaid had looked for a corner where he could find a bit of privacy, but not a foot of space was available anywhere. Then one

morning, as he lay on his hard, sagging bed gazing at
the ceiling, he spotted a trapdoor. Leaping out of
bed, he dragged a packing box under the door, put
a chair on the box and hoisted himself into a large
unfinished attic.

The problem of a "study" was solved then and
there. The attic had no floor, but by pushing some
loose boards together and by walking carefully, the
ingenious young scientist was able to keep from falling through the flimsy ceiling. By placing a couple of
boards across two nail kegs he made a table. A third
nail keg served as a chair. The pipe from the downstairs stove furnished enough heat to warm the attic
and to dry the botanical specimens. With a table, a
chair, a microscope, a stove, and hundreds of uniden-
tified specimens of plants and animals, Trevor was
content. Every free hour he could find, he worked in
the makeshift laboratory studying the plants and animals living in the Pribilofs, forms so different from
those he had previously known.

The students had left Stanford before the end of
the spring semester with the understanding that
they would complete their courses during the summer. With Dr. Jordan away, however, they refused to
open their books or to observe the seals. When he
returned unexpectedly, he found his young helpers
deep in card-playing, the books unopened, the pages
of their note-books untouched by pen or pencil.

Noticing that Kincaid was not a member of the
card-playing group, he asked, "Where's Kincaid?"

"Up in his laboratory," someone answered, rather
contemptuously, pointing toward the attic.

"His laboratory?" Jordan asked. Curious, the energetic, urbane President climbed onto the box and
squeezed his big body through the trapdoor. There

sat Kincaid, engrossed in the study of a bee. (The bee was later reported as a new species and given the name *Bombus kincaidii* by Dr. T. D. A. Cockerell.) Jordan sat down on the nail keg.

The two men talked for hours about the unsolved biological problems in this North country, not as master and student, but as scientific equals. How did one explain that foxes were common on this island, although they were not native here? How were they to account for the absence of whole orders of some insects and the abundance of others? Only one fly was noted, the *Syrphida,* which apparently was the principal agent in pollinating the local flora. The only butterfly was a yellow Pierid. In fact, there seemed no logic in the distribution of insects. Many beetles moved about in the tundra. Great flocks of seabirds blackened the skies and filled the air with their raucous cries. At the time there were no answers to many of these puzzling questions. They must be left to later scientists to solve, the men decided.

As Jordan was about to climb back to the world of card-players and seals, he said, "Trevor, you are the most energetic and industrious young man I have ever met. If you don't make your mark as a scientist, it won't be for lack of dedication."

Realizing he might never pass this way again, Kincaid could not bear to leave the most insignificant problem unexplored. Day after day he tramped through the tundra, walked along the rough beaches, or studied the disintegrating cinders of the volcanic soil. His mind was in a turmoil, seeking answers to his questions.

As R. E. Snodgrass, the only Stanford student interested in the work they were doing, and Kincaid helped corral the seals, they watched the great, powerful bulls herd the females into their harems, controlling them with rigid authority. The maneuvering and the constant roar of the seals as the fierce struggle for space and supremacy went on was astonishing both to hear and to see. To Kincaid it seemed the seals played out a drama unmatched in the complex story of animal behavior.

During the summer Kincaid made the finest friendship of his life, one he cherished always. Dr. D'Arcy Thompson, the British representative on the Fur Seal Commission, was a few years older than Trevor, but to his new friend he embodied the finest qualities of a scientist. As a student, he was broadly trained. In addition to his regular duties as a professor at the University of Dundee, he lectured at the University of Edinburgh; he had translated the natural history of Aristotle from Greek into English; he had written an extensive monograph on the relation of mathematical principles to the growth and forms of living organisms; he had published a series of papers on comparative anatomy; he had traveled extensively; and he knew most of the leading scientists of Europe.

To the young Westerner, a tramp across the tundra with Thompson was a rare experience, for every insect, every bird, every plant was familiar to him or reminded him of a story, an anecdote, or a bit of unusual information. Soon a fine rapport developed between the two men, and they often set out on long tramps across the rough volcanic soil or along the beaches, talking of many things—books, life, science, God, love—subjects a man shares only with a kindred spirit.

One rainy dull morning the two men climbed a steep hill leading to Mount Bogoslov. Suddenly the clouds parted, the sun broke through the mists, and as if by magic the verdure-clad slopes and jagged headlands stood out in all their beauty. In whichever direction they turned their heads there were flowers —here a patch of violets, there a clump of harebells, a slope bright with yellow poppies, a mass of blue gentians, rocks covered with red or yellow lichens, all ablaze in the short growing season. To Trevor the suddenly expanding landscape was like the unfolding of Thompson's mind and heart. For years he associated the two among his most beautiful memories.

As the two men continued their walk between the hills, they suddenly saw Mount Bogoslov, an extinct volcano several hundred feet high, lifting its head above them. In the minds of the natives some evil mystery was associated with the mountain. Apparently they believed that to approach it, to enter the hidden caves, or even to talk about them would bring some disaster to the island.

The scientists had no idea how far the caves extended or where they led, but, undaunted by superstition, they continued their climb. After considerable search they found an entrance to a cave and went in. To dissipate the darkness and the gloom they carried candles, and to help them retrace their steps, should they become lost, they unwound a ball of heavy twine which they dropped to the floor as they walked, expecting to pick it up as they returned through the dark passages. Eventually they found themselves in a large dome-shaped room with small holes at the top, apparently vents for the escape of volcanic gases.

A faint light filtered through the openings, showing the floor strewn with the skeletons of long-dead seals and polar bears, a graveyard unchanged perhaps for thousands of years. It was an eerie sight; it seemed likely that the cave had served as a den for bears during the Ice Age. Among other remains in the cave were the teeth and bones of a mammoth, a large extinct species of elephant. To ferret out an explanation for the presence of this animal on the Pribilof Island, Kincaid believed one would have to probe far back into geological history. Thompson and Kincaid did not attempt to explain the natives' fear of the mountain. It probably had its origin in some long-forgotten myth.

As the summer drew to a close and it became time for Thompson and Kincaid to part, Thompson suggested that Kincaid come to Scotland to teach for a year and that his assistant take Kincaid's work in Seattle. Kincaid could not accept this offer, however, because of family responsibilities.

As an acknowledgment of their friendship, Thompson, upon his return to England, sent Kincaid the fifty volumes of *The Challenger Reports,* that carefully written and beautifully illustrated set of books, which is often referred to as "The Holy Writ of Deep Sea Biology." *The Challenger's* aim, when it started out from England in 1872, had been "to learn everything about the sea." Of course it could not fulfill that ambitious dream, but when the ship returned four years later, it unquestionably brought back more information about the waters far below the surface than had been learned since Aristotle's time, and it formed the pattern for marine study for the next fifty years. In order that the students and faculty of the University of Washington might enjoy this remarkable work, Kincaid presented it to the University library.

By chance some years later a University of Washington scientist met D'Arcy Thompson in Scotland. Thompson asked, "How is Trevor Kincaid?" When the American scientist returned, he told Kincaid of his meeting with Thompson. Immediately Kincaid sent off a postcard to his old friend with the succinct message, "T. K. - O.K. D'A. T.- O.K?" Thompson fired back a reply, "D'A. T.-O.K. U.B.d.d. - T. K." (double-damned).

When the Russians first went to the Pribilofs in 1786 the Islands were uninhabited. They immediately realized the tremendous wealth that could be obtained from the skins of the seals that summered on the Islands. To secure workers to slaughter the seals and prepare the skins for market, the Russians brought in laborers from the Aleutian Islands, whose descendants continue to prepare the skins a hundred years later.

With the purchase of Alaska from the Russians in 1867, the Alaska Commercial Company was granted a monopoly of fur sealing in the Pribilofs for twenty years. At the time of Kincaid's stay on the Pribilofs, the Islands were administered rather like an Indian reservation, with the interests of the workers safeguarded in a paternalistic manner. The Aleuts had a monopoly on the work relating to the seals, but all moneys were paid into a fund administered by an agent of the United States government and distributed on a share basis, so that everyone, including widows, the elderly, the orphans, and the priest, received a proportionate share.

These sums were deposited to the credit of the various individuals and could be drawn upon at the store or through order catalogs. The natives were allowed to slaughter a quota of seals for food and to fish in the surrounding waters. At the time of Kincaid's visit to the Pribilofs the government agent was a genial though despotic man, the court of last appeal in all matters concerning the people.

Unfortunately, during the summer he was killed by a team of mules. A grave was hewn from the volcanic rock on a flower-strewn hillside with each man in the community taking his turn in raising a few shovelfuls of earth. With great masses of fog drifting across the landscape, the entire population of the island, as well as visiting scientists, gathered at the graveside to hear a government official read the burial service of the Church of England. As the mourners passed the open grave, each dropped a handful of earth into it. To add to the weirdness of the scene, Kincaid said, the roar of the sea and the ceaseless fighting and wailing of the seals was like a funeral dirge.

The United States Bureau of Fisheries assumed the management of the Pribilofs in 1910. (Yet, until 1949, the natives were virtual wards of the government, and even today they are not allowed to own their own land or govern their affairs. In 1966 an Aleut made a trip to Washington to present the problems of the 650 inhabitants to government authorities. Governor William A. Egan said, "Our treatment of these people is not a bright page in the history of the United States.")

Thus the summer sped by. The days began to shorten and the nights to cool. The bachelor seals, mostly three-year-olds, that were to furnish coats for fashionable women, had been killed and their pelts processed. The seal mothers had taught their young to fend for themselves and were preparing to set out with them on their long journey south. The old males, who had fasted since their arrival in May, went off to find food. The rookeries would remain empty and silent until the next spring when the seals would return; among them it was hoped would be those that had been branded. Kincaid explained that the number of tagged seals returning would indicate roughly the number of animals that had escaped the marauders during their journey to and from the tropics. Their gain in weight and the changes in their fur while in tropical waters would provide a measure of their general physical condition.

Dr. Jordan and the representatives of the countries involved in the study of the seals concluded their talks. On the basis of their discussions, treaties were signed by the several governments. The terms proved to be so carefully and fairly drawn up that the agreements have been honored for more than sixty years, during which time the number of seals on the Pribilof Islands has greatly increased. (Over the years, the U.S. government has earned enough seal-skin money to pay the purchase price of Alaska twenty times over.)

On the eve of the departure of the scientists, the Pribilof Islanders gave a dance in their honor. Dr. Jordan lead the grand march with the wife of the leading Aleut citizen. Towering almost a head above her, he bowed low and gave her his arm. The tiny lady, unaccustomed to such courtliness from her partners, scarcely knew what to do, but under the spell of Jordan's attention and polished manners, she was soon smiling and dancing gaily. Kincaid said in his *Autobiography* that for the second time in his life he regretted he had not learned to dance, for the music was so gay and rousing that his feet refused to stay still. (The first time was five years earlier when he had tapped his feet to the rhythm of the fiddle at the logging camp.)

When a few days later the government boat came to pick up the scientists, the islanders gathered on the shore to bid them farewell. Then the ship disappeared beyond the horizon and the natives turned back to the fog-shrouded village to await the coming of the long winter.

Standing on the deck watching the Pribilof Islands fade into the distance, Kincaid realized the summer had been of great value to him. It had given him an opportunity to satisfy some of his vast curiosity about the world. He had grown in understanding of men and nature; his concepts of the distribution of plant and animal life in the North Pacific had been greatly enlarged. Association with Dr. Jordan, D'Arcy Thompson, and other members of the scientific staff had given him tremendous admiration for the hearts and minds of educated, dedicated men. And, as his collections of Alaskan plants and animals went into the hands of specialists in many institutions, they brought him considerable recognition.

While the ship wound its way through the treacherous passages between the Aleutian Islands, Kincaid saw for the first time the volcanoes erupting, their flames turning the sky a brilliant red. He experienced a storm with winds blowing at 75 miles an hour. So vicious was the wind that the tossing and pitching of the vessel kept the men confined in the dark, airless bowels of the ship for three days. Even when the wind abated a bit, the fog was so dense that the craft looked like a phantom bobbing on the waters.

Kincaid left the government cutter at Dutch Harbor and returned to Seattle directly across the North Pacific, arriving a few days before the opening of the school year of 1897. He had taken another important step toward becoming a real scientist.

In 1899, two years after Trevor Kincaid went to the Pribilof Islands, he was invited to make a second trip to Alaska with E. H. Harriman, the wealthy Union Pacific Railroad magnate.

Mr. Harriman had planned to take his family to the North on a hunting expedition, but, considering the plan more closely, he decided that the cost of chartering a steamer solely for a pleasure trip was out of reason, even for a "sixty million dollar" tycoon. In his dilemma he talked to Dr. C. Hart Merriman, Chief of the United States Biological Survey, who suggested he enlarge both the purpose of the journey and its personnel to include scientists whose observations and collections of natural history materials would add to man's knowledge of the Far North.

Harriman agreed with the idea, increasing the group to 126 persons, 11 members of his family, 25 scientists, several artists, photographers, and taxidermists, as well as a large number of ship's officers and men. He leased the *George W. Elder*, a seagoing vessel, for a two-month voyage.

Assisting Mr. Harriman in the selection of scientists to accompany him to Alaska was Dr. Jordan, who gave Trevor Kincaid an excellent recommendation as an entomologist, as did Dr. L. O. Howard, chief of the United States Bureau of Entomology.

Of course Kincaid was flattered by this invitation, but that afternoon, as he made his way to the *Elder*, which was waiting for him at the foot of Seneca

Street in Seattle, he wished the ship could have sailed one day later. If that had been the case, instead of being dressed at that moment in boots and lumber jacket, he would have been resplendent in cap and gown receiving his Bachelor of Arts degree from President Graves. He had waited so long for this degree that it was disappointing not to experience the formality of having it bestowed upon him.

Yet pragmatist that he was, the slender, intense, bright-eyed young man realized that in the long view this scientific trip would be far more valuable to him than accepting a piece of parchment from the President's hand. He had done the work and the diploma would be waiting for him when he returned home. So, whistling "Purple and Gold," the new college song recently written by Isadora Singer, he hurried toward the boat.

The run north was a happy one with good weather and sunny skies. Mr. Harriman's combined hunting and scientific expedition was most luxurious. Everything possible had been provided for the use of the scientists: reference books, telescopes, microscopes, magnifying glasses, compasses, nets for catching insects, plant presses, bottles, alcohol for preserving specimens. Mr. Harriman was unquestionably the center and dynamo of the group, yet he was considerate and gracious to everyone, even the lowliest cabin boy.

In the almost five years since Kincaid had enrolled at the University of Washington as a conditioned freshman, his associates had changed from lumberjacks and oyster fishermen to some of the most famous "charming and elderly" scientists in the United States, among them John Muir, student of glaciers, naturalist, explorer, writer, and the real father of conservation; John Burroughs, the well-known nature writer; W. E. Ritter, professor of zoology at the University of California; Louis Agassiz Fortes, the distinguished artist, and other well-known scientists.

The ship did most of its traveling at night so that during the daylight hours the men could fan out from the big ship in small boats, for explorations of their own specialties—plants, animals, glaciers, geology. Everywhere the *Elder* stopped, Kincaid, a collecting kit over his shoulder, an ice pick in his hand, an insect net poised and ready for use, was off the ship almost before it was docked.

While the *Elder* was in the vicinity of the Muir Glacier, John Muir told many stories of his work with the glaciers. One incident he told impressed Kincaid deeply. When he was a young man, he suffered a severe accident to his eye, which made him fear it would be "closed forever to God's beauty." This fear had impelled him to make long treks on foot across the United States so that if he became blind, at least he would have a mental picture of his country; these cross-country tramps had indirectly inspired his writings. With his name given to the most spectacular of the Alaska glaciers, his memory would be perpetuated in the Far North, the land he loved.

In looking at the mammoth Muir Glacier, which flowed from Mount Fairweather to the sea, covering 350 miles, Kincaid visualized what Puget Sound must have looked like when it was buried under 5,000 feet of ice. He also realized a glacier was not necessarily devoid of life, for he discovered many small brown glacial worms, much like earthworms, living in the ice. These hardy little creatures buried themselves in the crevices of the glacier in an attempt to adapt to the new conditions of living. This they did by forming globules of water, which acted as antifreeze chambers and allowed them to melt their way through the ice as they searched for specks of organic food materials scattered about in the glacier.

Around Prince William Sound the glaciers had partially melted, leaving a large unexplored fjord, which gave the geologists an opportunity to study the area. As a courtesy to their host they called it "Harriman Fjord." Deep within the fjord they located a number of small glaciers, which they named Yale, Harvard, and Princeton, while a group of tiny ones became Smith, Vassar, and Radcliffe. Of course Kincaid was busy with his ice hammer and notebooks. Some of the sailors laughed at the youthful scientist confronting the mammoth glacier with his little tools.

At Ocra on Cook Island the retreat of the ice had produced plant life similar to that of the interior of Alaska. The forests had thinned out until the western end of the terrain looked like a park. Mr. Harriman decided this should prove an ideal hunting ground.

Since leaving the United States, he had become so engrossed in the work of Kincaid and the other scientists that he had not taken his firearms from their cases. But now, dressed in fashionable hunting attire, broad hat, baggy knickers, and high leather boots, he strutted across the open strip of land, ready to show his prowess as a hunter. An assortment of arms was brought out and ammunition readied.

The search for game began. The scouts, after beating the bushes for some time, sighted a small brown bear in the distance. With much fanfare, the animal was driven into a narrow passageway between two hills. Lest the "bear behave in an unpleasant manner," the gun bearers grouped themselves around Mr. Harriman with enough ammunition to tear the animal to bits.

All the precautions were unnecessary, for the killing was a very tame affair. One shot vanquished the prey. The bear fell dead without a protest, and without ceremony it was carried from the field of battle. The taxidermist took care of the bear, skinning and tanning the hide. Kincaid examined the entrails for parasites.

Of course, the killing of the bear, even a little frightened one, had to be properly celebrated by the distinguished hunter. A campsite was established near a beautiful waterfall, and sumptuous foods and drinks prepared. When the coffee was brewed, Mr. Harriman smacked his lips and took a deep swallow. Immediately he spat it out, demanding "What's the matter with the coffee"? The cook, it was discovered, had inadvertently made the coffee with salty water that had backed up from the sea with the tide into a reservoir. Later in the day Mary Harriman, the tycoon's daughter, shot a deer, thereby upholding the reputation of the family as hunters.

At Kukak Bay, a peninsula north of Kodiak, Kincaid found a profusion of flowers and swarms of beautiful swallowtail butterflies, *Papilio macheon.* In lieu of a microscope, he used a hand lens on field trips, noticing the minutest markings of a butterfly's wings or the turn of the sepals of a flower. He kept a detailed record of when, where, and by whom each specimen had been collected. "Leave nothing to memory" was his infallible rule.

He was delighted to discover fossils of leaves and flowers that in the nineteenth century grew only in the southern part of the United States, a striking example of the changes that continually take place on the surface of the earth. These delicate engravings in stone represented the Miocene period of geological history when Alaska had a subtropical climate. At the end of each day when Kincaid returned to the ship with his collecting boxes filled with specimens, Mr. Harriman would say, "Show me what you found today."

When the *Elder* left for Unalaska, the Pribilofs, and Port Clarence, areas Kincaid had visited on his earlier trip to the Pribilof Islands, he remained on the Shumagin Islands, planning to rejoin the ship on the Popof Islands two weeks later. Six of the young sailors went with him to help him collect, arrange specimens, establish camps, and prepare meals.

Kincaid was elated at the prospect of two full weeks of freedom from the routine of the ship. While on his private safari he would be able to study the plants and animals in much greater detail than he had been able to on the usual short stops. But the best part of the interlude was a reprieve from the formality of life aboard a millionaire's ship. For two precious weeks he did not have to shave or wear a white shirt and necktie for meals or keep up a sprightly conversation with his table mates. He gave himself wholly to the materials he was collecting.

Each morning he set out on a foray of collecting, returning with dozens of hitherto unknown specimens. While on the Shumagin Islands he discovered so many plants that Dr. Hultan, a Swedish botanist, said he had extended the range of known Bering Sea flora by 500 miles. Dr. Hultan later used the plants as the basis of a book on the plant life of Alaska.

As Darwin had done on the Galápagos Islands two-thirds of a century before, here in the Shumagin Islands Kincaid "began to form a coherent view of life on this planet." He had come a long way from the teachings of the Methodist preacher in Peterborough.

The two weeks passed quickly and the *Elder* was back to pick up Kincaid and his helpers. The summer expedition was almost over. The party set out for Seattle. The lower deck of the ship was partitioned into laboratories where the scientists could spread and arrange their specimens. Kincaid's bottles, jars, and nets spilled out into the passageways. Mr. Harriman said, "I had no idea that investigating glaciers, ice worms, fossils, and insects could be so interesting. Really much more worth while than shooting bears." Of Trevor Kincaid he said, "During the entire two months, he was never out of temper or said a hasty word to anyone." This was a great tribute, Trevor thought. In 1938 the journals of John Muir were published. In speaking of the talks given by scientists present on the Harriman Expedition, Muir wrote, "Young Kincaid's address on insects was one of the best of the trip. He has genius and will be heard of later, I hope."

Dropping anchor in Seattle during the first drenching rain of September, Kincaid pulled his cap lower over his forehead, wrapped his coat closer around his shoulders, and hurried to President Graves' office to pick up his University of Washington diploma. In welcoming him back, Graves patted him on the back and said, "We made you an assistant professor while you were away." The young biologist had reached the next rung on the professional ladder.

Study on the plants and animals Kincaid had gathered in Alaska was by no means completed. First he had to arrange the specimens according to phyla, a vast undertaking in itself. Then he had to check and verify them as to family, genus, and species. If he could not do this with certainty, he would send them to specialists in the United States National Museum in Washington. As a final check, he would seek the aid of experts in Europe in identifying the most baffling specimens.

All winter Kincaid worked on this exacting job whenever he had a free minute. Although by the end of the school year, he believed he had become an authority on several groups of insects and could make the final classifications himself, the inadequate facilities of the University library made it necessary for him to seek help with the classifications, so he spent the following summer in Washington, D.C., completing the work.

Scientists who saw the 8,000 specimens Kincaid had collected were amazed that one man could have gathered them all. This huge collection represented 1,000 species of insects, including 237 new species of Hymenoptera and 63 new species of Diptera (flies). Eleven were named after Kincaid. The final report of the expedition was published in a sumptuous series of 17 volumes called *The Harriman Alaska Expedition, 1899;* two of them were devoted exclusively to Kincaid's papers on insects. At that time Kincaid's collection of insects was the largest ever brought from Alaska, and it is probably one of his major contributions to science.

While Kincaid was in Washington, he received an invitation from Mr. Harriman to spend the weekend with his family in Arden, New York, but he declined, saying to himself, "I might be expected to wear white tie and tails."

The work Kincaid had done on the Harriman Expedition established him as a highly able scientist. Although only 26 years old, he received much recognition in the nation's capital because of the collections he had made on the Pribilof Islands and on the Harriman Expedition. In fact he was then regarded as one of the world's eminent young entomologists. Yet Kincaid's knowledge was not confined to insects; he was well informed on many phases of biological study.

Through his wide correspondence he had gained a considerable reputation in scientific circles in England. An amusing incident occurred when a party of British scientists, including Lord Lister, Curator of the British Museum and a brother of Joseph Lister, the founder of antiseptic surgery, came to Seattle after attending a medical meeting in Victoria, British Columbia. The British dignitaries were escorted about the city by a committee of the King County Medical Association. After they had shown Lord Lister the beauties of Seattle and introduced their learned guest to the leading citizens, Lister inquired of one of the doctors, "How can I get in touch with Trevor Kincaid"?

The doctor leaned over to one of his fellow physicians and whispered hoarsely, "Who the hell is Trevor Kincaid?" He was evidently not a prophet with honor in his own country.

Even if Kincaid was not known to the physicians of Seattle, to the students of the University of Washington he was acknowledged not only as an eminent scientist but as the most popular and versatile man on the campus, who could even turn his hand to writing poetry. For the first edition of the *Tyee*, University yearbook, published in 1900, he wrote "The Epitaph of a Fern."

Years later when asked about his poetry-writing days, he laughed, "I didn't know anything about iambic pentameters, trochees or symbols. Apparently the editors of the *Tyee* didn't either, for they kept asking me for my gems." Then his voiced boomed out and he quoted:

> Deep in the mountain rough and gray
> A lonely hillside stands.
> In chinks and nooks wild flowers play,
> Waving in gleaming bands.
>
> Among the rest a dainty fern
> Springs from the jagged slope.
> Its whispering fronds to heaven turn
> As it casts its spores about.
>
> Hurled forth in rapid flight,
> One circles through the air,
> But falls at last in a crevice tight
> 'Neath moss and lichens rare.
>
> Out of the wall from its hidden nest,
> Soothed by the balmy air
> The little stranger lifts its crest,
> A miracle most fair.
>
> For months the fernlet waxed and grew.
> A fluttering song of joy,
> And then, alas, cold breezes blew
> And tricked it to destroy.

By that time Kincaid's reputation for knowing the answers to all manner of questions had become widely known. He was becoming a Seattle oracle. No matter how foolish the question or how much time it took from his already crowded schedule, he answered each with equal courtesy and care.

As early as 1900 he was material for amusing stories, relating to his "bug-catching" or his absent-mindedness. One story that made the rounds of the campus for years arose when automobiles and gas-lights were novelties in the University District. One night when the professor was crossing the street at East 45th and 14th Avenue Northeast (University Way), on his way home from his midnight vigil in his office, he saw a number of moths flying around the hissing arc lights. One especially beautiful creature in its frenzy dashed against the light and fell to the ground, its splendid wings crumpled and broken. Kincaid stooped to pick it up.

As it happened, rowdies in the area had been puncturing automobile tires by putting nails in the street. Just as Kincaid bent down to pick up the moth, a policeman hurried up to him.

"What are you up to?" the officer demanded, grabbing him by the arm.

"I just picked up a moth," Kincaid answered innocently.

"That's a likely story. Come with me," ordered the officer.

"Here it is. You can see for yourself," said Kincaid. "I teach zoology at the University and I pick up lots of butterflies and moths."

"Where do you live?" the policeman demanded, holding Kincaid's arm tighter.

"Just around the corner on Brooklyn Avenue," the puzzled young man answered.

"Come along. I'll see you get there," the policeman said skeptically.

Together the two men walked toward Brooklyn

Avenue. Reaching the door, Kincaid took the key from his pocket, put it in the lock, and opened the door.

"Well, goodnight," said the defender of the law. "Guess you're telling the truth. But I suggest you forget about hunting moths at midnight. Next time you might not get off so easily."

CHAPTER 5

Trevor Kincaid and
the University Grow Up

TREVOR KINCAID did not spend all his time on expeditions or in his laboratory. As he advanced in rank in the University hierarchy, he became interested in the affairs of the school, although he refused to become a partisan in disputes.

Edwards and Reeves, the itinerant Presidents, as Kincaid called them, remained in office less than a year each. With their going, the Regents amended their idea that "a man with moderate talents but one faithful and deserving" was better than a brilliant scholar by selecting Frank Pierpont Graves, one of the best-educated and youngest presidents in the country, to head the University of Washington. Although not 30 years of age, Graves held a bachelor's degree from Boston University, and a Doctor of Science degree from Heidelberg College in Ohio. He had spent a year in graduate work at Harvard, had been instructor in Greek at Tufts, and had served for two years as President of the University of Wyoming.

The inauguration of Graves as President of the University of Washington was impressive. It was held in Denny Hall, November 30, 1898, with music, speeches, and flowers. David Starr Jordan, the featured orator of the day, proclaimed the coming of Graves to the University a great step forward, "a milestone in her pilgrimage." (In his *Autobiography,* Kincaid recalled how that morning he had shined Jordan's shoes after he had stepped into a puddle of mud on his way to the exercises.)

The young, ambitious president, in his response to Jordan's glowing tribute, spoke of the bright future of the University, thereby instilling confidence into the audience and the citizens of the state. A number of delicate problems confronted Graves soon after his inauguration. One of these was the status of Edmond Meany, an 1885 graduate of the University, a legislator, and a staunch friend of the school.

Meany, tall, handsome, charming, a man who offered a helping hand to everyone, had become involved in politics. With the removal of the University to its new location in 1895, Meany had been given the non-academic position of Registrar. During two years in the legislature, he had become interested in local history, and was soon teaching a course dealing with the early days of the Northwest. He also loved the outdoors, was president of the Mountaineer Club, and taught a course in forestry. Although he had no training in either history or forestry, he had gained a toehold in the academic life of the University and he was eager to keep it. He had bitterly opposed John R. Rogers, the Populist candidate for Governor, during the violent campaign of 1896. After the Populists won by a landslide, Meany was definitely in disfavor.

Kincaid was much concerned by Meany's predicament, for since his first meeting with him in 1894, Meany had helped him in many ways. Yet of the campaign Kincaid said, "When the smoke had cleared away, Rogers was Governor and Meany was, in a sense, on the end of a limb and Rogers had the saw to cut off the branch."

Rogers had promised not to interfere in the affairs of the University, but he could not resist reorganizing the Board of Regents. Feeling was running high against Meany, and the new Regents refused to reappoint him.

Meany, not believing the Regents would dismiss him, went to the Governor and almost on his knees reviewed his loyalty to the University and promised to refrain from taking any further part in politics. Rogers agreed to take no direct action against him but to leave the matter up to the Regents and President Graves.

In support of his cause, Meany took into President Graves' office a sheaf of clippings and scrapbooks showing favorable publicity he had written concerning the University. After weeks of indecision, Graves recommended Meany's reinstatement. The Regents supported the President by a single vote.

At the height of the argument, Governor Rogers had said, "I presume there are in the State of Washington a hundred persons as fully qualified to teach history as is Mr. Meany." Actually, the records showed there were 76 applicants for the position, at least half of whom had academic training far superior to Meany's.

Kincaid knew that President Graves was astute enough to recognize that a state university needed many things besides academic degrees, that few persons knew the University and the state as Edmond Meany did, and that no one was more devoted and loyal to their welfare. Before the controversy was settled, it became evident that Meany did not owe his position to the good will of the Governor, his own loyalty, or his favorable public image. He owed it to President Graves' determination to resist political pressures. The President was fighting for independence and academic freedom.

Without question, Meany's experience further convinced Kincaid to steer clear of political partisanship or any type of party adherence. For the hundredth time he thanked his lucky stars that his love of the outdoors and his unswerving determination to become a first-rate scientist kept him remote from the foibles of his fellow men. However, at that time the wisdom of such detachment was debatable. Some outspoken adherents to a cause considered Kincaid's neutral position a lack of involvement in the institution.

Back in the University by the narrowest of margins, Meany knew that if he were to take his place on a par with men who held master's and doctor's degrees from Eastern universities, he would have to go to an Eastern school for further training. He first asked himself whether his primary interest was in history or forestry. He chose history. Although he spent several summers at the University of Wisconsin, he was not granted a degree there. Yet, in his subsequent long years of service on the Washington faculty, Meany, true to his word, assiduously shunned politics. He became one of the most energetic chroniclers of early Northwest events and published more than fifty books and articles. Through the years he became the "Grand Old Man" of the University and the "Keeper of Traditions." It was often said that he was more than a part of the University; he *was* its spirit and inner force.

Graves' administration, as had been predicted, was one of growth and change. He took over a school of about 300 and four years later it was almost three times that size. Kincaid laughingly recalled that the President's goal was to raise the enrollment to a thousand. He could not quite muster that number, but he would not give up his dream. In a final desperate effort he suggested to his secretary that she open the city directory, lift the necessary number of names, and insert them in the University roster. The next catalog listed 1001 names.

Prior to Graves' administration there had been few if any social events in which the student body as a whole could participate. Now students were carried away with every kind of get-together. Paper chases were a popular form of party. For a paper chase, Kincaid explained, the students, as many as wished to participate, gathered at Denny Hall on a moonlight night. Here they tore newspapers into strips a foot or two long and about six inches wide. These were given to a group of students who dashed through the woods north of Denny Hall, running around trees and across open spaces, casting the papers in all directions. Approximately half an hour later, the rest of the party hurried off to find them, using for clues the scattered pieces of paper. When the paper scatterers were found, the pot of gold at the end of the trail was a box of apples and a bag of cookies.

Athletics became tremendously important. Track, a sport that required no special equipment, attracted many of the boys. After an unusually successful season in 1899 in which Joe Pearson, a 16-year-old boy wonder, ran the 100-yard dash in ten seconds, a charge of hiring trackmen became a matter of dispute.

Trevor Kincaid laughed at the suggestion of professionalism in the track team, because he had helped train it. During his logging camp days he had thought nothing of hiking twenty miles; when he reported for a physical examination at the University, the doctor found his chest expansion to be six and a half inches, "the expansion of an athlete."

Professor van de Vere, the track coach, persuaded him to set the pace for the daily workout of the relay team. After running a mile or two, the boys stopped trying to keep up with their leader. At the end of the fourth or fifth mile they fell to the ground panting, while Kincaid was still "fresh as a daisy."

By the turn of the century football had become the great American college sport. Kincaid said many parents frowned upon it, however, because after almost every game the *Pacific Wave*, an early college paper, reported the not altogether reassuring item that "the patients were improving." The University had for its coach the remarkable Gil Dobie. During his nine years (1908–17) as coach, his team won 58, tied 3, and lost none.

The baseball team made a trip to Japan, winning 6 games and losing 2. Basketball, too, had its bright moments. Even the girls had an intercollegiate team in 1896; in one game they won over Ellensburg Normal in two 15-minute halves, with two baskets to Ellensburg's one. The *Pacific Wave* warned the girls against "overtraining, for some of the girls showed extreme nervousness."

But it was rowing that caught and held the attention and enthusiasm of the students and citizens of Seattle. This was due in part, Kincaid believed, to the University being located directly on beautiful Lake Washington, and in part to the mild winters, which allowed for training throughout the year. When Hiram Conibear, who had been brought to Seattle as a football trainer and track coach, was asked to take

Trevor Kincaid and other students helping to beautify the campus in front of Denny Hall. The University was moved to its present location in 1895, and Denny Hall was built that year.

Trevor Kincaid setting the pace for a relay race in 1910. He had a chest expansion of six inches then.

over the rowing crew, he frankly admitted he didn't know one end of a boat from the other, but he said, "I'll try."

At first Conibear coached the rowing crews by shouting and bluffing, "to make up in noise what I lacked in knowledge," he confessed. After a couple of years of study of the techniques and experimentation with shells and strokes, he became one of the outstanding coaches in the United States and brought many championships to the University.

Mandolin and glee clubs visited nearby towns, announcing their arrival with street parades, complete with banners, blaring horns, and college yells.

Trevor Kincaid took great interest in debates and oratorical contests because he still believed a man's ability to express his ideas before an audience was important to his future success. Through the years he became a polished speaker and gave hundreds of lectures before all types of groups.

Probably the longest and most heated discussion waged during President Graves' administration was in regard to the establishment of college dormitories. Opinion, according to Kincaid, was strongly divided as to their merits. The principal argument against them was that dormitory life was unnatural and sterile. The argument that finally tipped the scales in their favor was that the buildings would be as well furnished and comfortable as possible for the sum expended, each with its own living area, dining room, and kitchen. In short, the residence halls would provide a homelike atmosphere and encourage students from all parts of the state to come to the University. In the end, Lewis and Clark Halls were built, one for men and one for women, each to accommodate 130 persons. Charges for board and room were eight to ten dollars per month.

Martha Lois Hansee was appointed Dean of Women and matron of the dormitory. For some reason President Graves became dissatisfied with her management of the halls and eager to find a way to dismiss her. To obtain evidence of her careless supervision of the residences, he made an unannounced inspection of them. His critical comments on their untidy condition incurred the wrath of the girls.

The next morning the girls and their mothers marched to Graves' office armed with brooms, mops, and dishpans, singing a parody of "We kept a pig in the parlor." The inspection backfired, with criticism falling upon Graves rather than upon Miss Hansee and the girls. Kincaid deeply regretted this undignified behavior on the part of the President. The *Seattle Star* gave the incident front-page headlines. Governor Rogers called it "remarkable, unusual and out of place," and held the President responsible for it.

Until this time the students had idealized President Graves, but the embarrassing encounter with the girls showed how fragile student popularity was. He never regained the confidence of the student body. Criticism of his other policies, most of it minor, followed. The sum total of the charges was that he could not enforce discipline and create a cooperative spirit. Kincaid's conclusion was that Graves' principal trouble arose from his desire to please everyone, which in the end pleased no one.

To counteract the idea that living in a dormitory was bleak and unnatural, Miss Hansee sponsored a number of social events—dancing parties, teas in honor of the Regents, and "sociable evenings" for the junior class in the home of President and Mrs. Graves. The *Wave* always reported, "The evening was spent with games and pleasant conversation. At the close of the evening ice cream and cake were served."

The President was firmly convinced that social life should be stressed on the campus and urged the professors to invite students to their homes. This suggestion did not elicit much response, for there was little permanence or security in a faculty appointment, and the pay was a mere pittance.

When Horace Byers applied for the position of head of the chemistry department, Graves said, "I hope you are married or soon will be."

Byers stammered, "No, I'm not married and have no prospects for such a step at this time."

Graves answered, "My main reason for desiring a married man is that we are overrun already with twelve bachelors, which shifts the burden of entertaining on a few professors. Yet it is necessary our students should learn the usages of good society. Therefore, for the present I insist that new members of the faculty be married men." Graves hinted to Kincaid it might be well if he married, but he answered, "That is a luxury I cannot afford. I now have three women in my life—my mother and two sisters."

Some time later Byers returned to the campus with a bride, who eventually, with the help of six daughters, dutifully served cake and ice cream to all and sundry students.

As a further reaction against the drab early days of the University, the students organized dancing clubs, honor societies, and discussion groups. Soon sororities and fraternities flooded the campus. By 1902 seven Greek-letter houses had been organized. Two years later there were ten, with 160 members out of an eligible enrollment of 700 students.

When the chapter of Sigma Nu was installed on the campus, Kincaid was asked to become a member. He did not affiliate with the group because at the time he thought fraternities were undemocratic and snobbish and caused young men to waste their time, although later he admitted they had a number of good points. As an example of the time consumed by such organizations, he cited a member of the senior class who belonged to Delta Upsilon, Phi Alpha Delta, Sigma Upsilon, Oval Club, Dramatic Association, Stevens-Badger Debate Society, Senior Kirniss, Junior Girls' Vaudeville group, the Law Association, Law School Debate Team, and Varsity Debate Team.

In the end extra-curricular activities came almost to control the University. An early issue of the *Alumnus* reported that a professor asked, "What is the matter with the University?" John F. Condon of the Law School answered, "Too much society. Too many social events. Too many young men and women wasting their time 'queening.' The fraternity students almost shape the social life of the school and are responsible for these evils." Dean Priest summed up the situation by saying, "The men are girl crazy."

Inevitably, as Kincaid had predicted, along with fraternities, sororities, and unrestricted social life came the other side of University life—hazing, kangaroo courts, rowdyism, fights, plus poor scholarship. Graves did his best to put an end to these practices, but to no avail.

Looking at the development of the University as a whole, Kincaid said, "In spite of the emphasis upon the froth of University life during Graves' administration, many solid advances were made." The schools of law, pharmacy, engineering, and mines were authorized. The liberal arts curriculum, revised and strengthened, remained the core of the whole. A balance of required and elective courses was outlined, thus resolving a debate of long standing. The study of Latin and Greek as requirements for a bachelor's degree was removed and modern languages were substituted. The Associated Student Association was set up to handle student activities in 1901.

Several attempts had been made to inaugurate a graduate school. In 1899 master's degrees were bestowed upon four students, including Edmond Meany. Although the master's program was beset by many problems, it was continued. President Graves also experimented with the granting of the Ph.D. degree, but this was soon dropped. He also wisely recommended that the conferring of honorary degrees be discontinued. He favored some arrangement for establishing sabbatical leaves, but no feasible arrangement was devised until much later.

By 1901 the student body had completely outgrown the 20,000 square feet of floor space in Denny Hall, which only a few years earlier had been thought sufficient for many years to come. Through a vigorous campaign in the legislature led by Graves, the University secured $60,000 for a science building and $50,000 for a power house.

The three-story science building of red pressed brick with sandstone trimmings was completed in 1902. Kincaid was very proud of the first- and second-story semi-circular laboratories similar to those allotted to the zoology department in Denny Hall. The chemistry and physics departments, which for years had been housed in small portable buildings, moved into the new science building. Lecture and classroom spaces were ample in the new building, but no funds had been provided for laboratory equipment. The surveying course, the only work being offered in the newly organized engineering school, had to borrow chains, levels, metallic wires, and transits from the city of Seattle for practical work.

About this time Graves proudly remarked, "The phenomenal growth of the University proves that we have seized upon the true ideal of college life. And I hope to put in most of my career in building up this University." His hope was not to be fulfilled, for during the next few months a succession of incidents occurred that blasted this dream, most of them involving his lack of rapport with the students.

When he showed a spark of independence by writing a 35-page report in which he went into detail on a number of matters that he thought rightly came under his authority, but which the Regents considered within their jurisdiction, his tenure became exceedingly precarious.

In his report he pointed out that the large increase in enrollment was due to the 300 lectures he had given within two years to citizens of the state who had seldom or never heard of the University. Even this did not help him. Kincaid said that such a heated discussion arose that within a twelve-month period (1902) Graves was asked to resign.

Trevor Kincaid gave little attention to the selection of Thomas Kane as president following the dismissal of President Graves. As usual, considerable politics and ill feeling had been involved in Kane's appointment. But politics, even those within the halls of academe, were not for Kincaid. His was a world of science, and neither politics, social striving, nor money could lure him from the road he had set for himself.

The life of a scientist, he felt, is entirely devoted to scientific investigations and is usually a quiet one. Startling adventures have little place in it. Trevor Kincaid was more than content to devote himself to the inquiries and experiments of his day in the solitude of his laboratory.

Thomas Kane, a scholar trained at Johns Hopkins University, had been a professor of Latin at the University of Washington and a co-worker of President Graves. He was appointed as executive officer with the understanding he would serve only a few months, while the Regents looked for a man who would have no superior in the field of education, "A man who in all respects would fill the requirements which an institution of this character deserves." Nevertheless, Kane's appointment lasted eleven years, the longest in the history of the University to date.

One of his first problems was remedying the imbalance between work and play at the University. At the first assembly after he became President, Kane outlined what he expected of entering freshmen. For several years the freshmen had been free to do whatever they pleased, completely ignoring the mores of their predecessors, which of course meant there was no sense of tradition or loyalty to hold the school together.

By this time everyone, even the students themselves, admitted there was too little studying and too much gaiety. In a single year 100 students were requested not to return to the University, and 250 were taken back on probation out of a student body of scarcely more than 1,000. With so little attention given to serious college work, only a small percentage completed their studies. Kincaid said the number of "quituates" was far greater than the number of "graduates."

The upper classmen, rallying to Kane's program, soon made it known that freshmen who violated the rules for study and class attendance would have to run on their hands and knees a gantlet of sophomores armed with shillelaghs. A third-time offender would be drawn in a little red wagon to the front of the Administration Building, then forced to run through the shillelagh line, carted to the lake, and dumped in.

In a further effort to combat the overemphasis upon the "froth" of University life, the faculty suggested a Student Assembly be formed to sponsor activities not strictly within the sphere of official University responsibilities. At first, funds were raised by individual subscriptions and fund-raising ventures. Later at Kincaid's suggestion the students secured approval for a fifty-cent fee collected from everyone for the support of student activities. The following year "The Associated Students" was organized; it has been the basis of student government ever since.

Thomas Kane was not the nationally recognized educator the Regents had hoped to get for President, but his qualifications, according to Charles Gates, were a thorough training, sterling character, infinite patience, painstaking care of detail, and considerable astuteness in sensing administrative needs. Trevor Kincaid said that he was not particularly skilled in currying favor with politicians, but he won the good will of the faculty by allowing them to conduct their own departments, asking their help in forming policies, giving them a voice in reaching conclusions, and particularly by insisting that study was the primary object of a University student.

He gained the support of the business interests and the citizens of the state by incorporating the practical problems of the Northwest into the University program. A Department of Oriental Studies was organized under Dr. H. H. Gowen to encourage study of languages and literature of the Asiatic countries with which the Northwest shared interests. A Department of Scandinavian Languages was set up under Dr. Edwin Vickner at the request of the many Scandinavians in the area. And the Marine Station was organized in 1904 by Trevor Kincaid, who recognized the tremendous wealth of marine life in Puget Sound and surrounding waters.

University geologists made topographical and hydrographical surveys; sanitary engineers worked with sewage and disposal problems; hydraulic engineers studied water supplies; chemists and physicists tested the strength of cement, wire cable, and timber; foresters assisted in timber surveys, logging operations, and fire control; mining engineers gave advice in methods of efficient coal production; botanists and zoologists demonstrated methods of combating Canadian thistle, diseases of fish, and the dangers of over-fishing. It was at this time that Kincaid began serving the citizens of the state, an activity that was to consume much of his time.

Probably nothing the University had ever done helped build as favorable a public image as did these services. Yet when the President spoke to the students, he always declared that higher education should, first of all, provide a general cultural training, and at the same time prepare them to take their places in some useful profession or industry important to the up-building of the state.

Kane realized that strong loyalties had never developed at the University, owing largely to the continual comings and goings of the Presidents, the dominating attitudes of the Board of Regents, the procession of teachers, the absence of stable traditions, and the as yet voiceless alumni group. The low salaries and the continuous need of money to operate the University, too, accounted for many of the difficulties. As head of the zoology department, Kincaid was paid $1,000 a year; assistant professors with families received $1,200; unmarried instructors with Ph.D. degrees earned $1,000. Kane said the salary scale was one of the lowest in the United States. "With such salaries, it is very difficult to attract men of ability and training," the President contended.

The greatest challenge to an expanding University, he maintained, lay not in acquiring new professors but in keeping them happy by giving them adequate salaries, reasonable teaching schedules, promotions, and good library facilities. In his *Autobiography,* Kincaid said that under Graves and Kane, in spite of troublesome student discipline, the University attracted a number of capable, well-trained men. Between 1903 and 1905 Kane appointed thirty men to the faculty. Of these, sixteen had earned Ph.D. degrees from leading American universities and one from a German university.

Men like Vernon Parrington, David Thompson, Robert Moritz, C. E. Magnusson, William Savery, J. Allen Smith, Fredrick Morgan Padelford, Allen Benham, Herbert H. Gowen, Charles Weaver, Edgar Loew, Charles W. Harris, Milnor Roberts, George W.

Umphrey, and Horace Byers formed the nucleus of a faculty whose morale was high and whose faith in Washington was always confident and optimistic. "It was the Golden Age of scholastic advancement," said Kincaid.

With men of high caliber taking their places on the campus, and with an ever-expanding program of courses and diversified subject matter, Kincaid began to wonder if he should seek education beyond that which he had received in this new western university. He had taken a bachelor's degree in 1899 and a master's degree in 1901, and although he was considered an authority in entomology and had a tremendous fund of general biological information, he had never studied in such centers of learning as Harvard or Yale, as had many of his colleagues. To an outsider he knew the zoology department seemed very weak and small. Once, when he was on a trip to California, someone asked, "Who is the head of the department?" He answered, "I am. In fact, I am both the head and the foot."

Professor Foster, who had been brought to Seattle to take Professor Hill's place when he went East to finish his medical course, stayed at the University but two years. When Charles Hill decided not to return to Seattle after receiving his medical degree, the biology department was left without a chairman. In 1903, Theodore Frye came to the University to take Foster's place. Since Frye was not prepared to teach zoology, the biology department was permanently divided. Frye accepted the headship of the botany department, and Kincaid became chairman of the zoology department. To Kincaid the separation of the departments was a fortunate arrangement, for it made him his own boss. He realized too that his and

Frye's temperaments were quite unlike and that the separation of their work would probably forestall animosity.

Now that he was in charge of the zoology work on the campus, Kincaid felt more certain than ever that he should test his knowledge of zoology and of university procedures against those of other zoologists and other centers of learning. He applied for an Austin Fellowship at Harvard, which was quickly granted. He then asked for a leave of absence from the University, and Dr. C. W. Prentice, a graduate of Harvard, was brought to Seattle to take over his work.

Kincaid spent the summer at the Bermuda Biological Station, which was under the auspices of Harvard. Here he studied the subtropical fauna of the southern waters with its profusion of seafans, corals, brilliant-colored fish, and large mollusks, forms that had formerly been unfamiliar to him. The summer in Bermuda passed quickly, and then Kincaid went to Harvard, where he enrolled in courses in comparative anatomy, cellular biology, genetics, and research problems.

Instead of being assigned to private research rooms in which to work, as he had expected, the graduate students were given desks in one large room. To make sure the talkative students did not disturb the more studious ones, "NO TALKING" signs were posted here and there about the room. To Kincaid, the room resembled a Trappist monastery, but it was not long before he found kindred spirits. The graduate students in zoology had been trained in schools scattered across the country and had come from a variety of backgrounds, many of them with far wider experience of the world than he had had.

And certainly they made up for their lack of conversation in the laboratory by animated talk in the
Commons at noon. A dozen or more very vocal
young men gathered around a lunch table where,
over their beans and brown bread, they punctuated
their arguments with table-pounding and fist-shak-
ing. With members of this group Kincaid visited art
galleries, historical sites, and concert halls. These extra-curricular activities added much to his cultural
education, which he said had been sadly neglected.
"At least they were different from logging-camp
dances and dinners of octopus chowder and seaweed." But even the culture of Boston and the ele-
gant young men with whom he associated could not
change his careless habits of dress. His cowlick was
just as wayward and his trousers just as water-stained
from hunting specimens in the muddy ponds in Boston as they had been in Seattle.

The Museum of Comparative Zoology and the library associated with it, donated in large part to Harvard by Louis Agassiz and his son Alexander, gave
Kincaid his greatest excitement and pleasure. No expense had been spared in assembling the displays in
the museum and keeping them up to date. During
the later years of his life, Alexander Agassiz had
amassed great wealth through investments in copper
mines in Michigan, and he had given more than a
million dollars to the museum.

At the time Kincaid attended Harvard, the museum was probably one of the finest natural history
museums in the world, though it was unusual in being organized by continents rather than by phyla of
animals, as were most museums. It was arranged thus
because Louis Agassiz did not believe in evolution.
He held firmly to the idea that each species of animal

had been created at one time in the number and
distribution it still had. He was one of Darwin's most
bitter critics, fighting his theory to the end of his life.
His son, Alexander, said he would wait until he had
more evidence before accepting or rejecting the theory.

It was with real regret that Kincaid packed his bags
and his bottles of insects in the spring of 1906 and
took the train for Seattle. The year in Cambridge had
put many things into proper perspective in his mind.
Above all, it had given him confidence in his own
abilities and scientific knowledge. He knew that on
entomological questions he could hold his own in any
discussion. As is true of many a traveler, Kincaid had
no sooner discovered what was most interesting at
Harvard than it was time to leave it.

During Kincaid's absence from the University,
President Kane had made Dr. Prentice a permanent
member of the zoology department. Until this time
the meager finances of the school had not allowed
the addition of extra teachers. Now with someone to
assume some of the teaching load, Kincaid was eager
to offer a course under the title of "Museum and
Field Work."

Ever since his childhood, when he had invited the
citizens of Peterborough to view his collections in his
father's barn, he had been fascinated with museums.
Remembering the vast number of plants and animals
collected by the members of the Young Naturalists'
Society, Dr. Orson Bennett Johnson's huge collection, and his own thousands of specimens, brought
this interest to a head, and Kincaid put them all on
display in the University of Washington. Kincaid's
next innovation was to sponsor a course in Indian
culture, which laid the foundation of the Depart-

ment of Anthropology. Similarly, the School of Fisheries was the outgrowth of a course he gave in fish diseases. Instruction in all departments of the University was on the move, but he was usually a step ahead of his colleagues.

During the years of President Thomas Kane's leadership (1902–1913), the University of Washington took long strides toward growing up, and made steady progress toward taking its place on a par with other Western state universities. Nonetheless, during the last year of his presidency, a host of problems came to plague the quiet, hard-working man. A lack of communication between the Regents and the President resulted in a demand for his resignation. The Board told him, "The University has outgrown you." Charles Gates quotes a member of the Board as saying, "The Board of Regents desires a big man to head the University, a man of stature and distinction, possessed of personal magnetism, a gift of oratory, a man who can play the role of President brilliantly and who can focus attention of the University upon himself." Obviously, neither Thomas Kane nor any other man could fill all these requirements.

In 1971 a recently constructed building on the campus was dedicated to the memory of Thomas Kane, who did so much to bring the University to maturity. On the day the building was to be dedicated, President Odegaard told the author of this book that he had known almost nothing about Thomas Kane, his predecessor at the University by almost fifty years, until December, 1969, when he had gone to the home of Trevor Kincaid to congratulate him on attaining his ninety-seventh birthday and to tell him that the Regents had voted to name the new biology building Trevor Kincaid Hall.

On that occasion Kincaid had told him many interesting facts about the early days of the University. Among these were accounts of Kane's outstanding contributions to the school. On the basis of these remarks, Dr. Odegaard decided to recommend to the Regents that the new building be named Kane Hall in recognition of his years of devoted service.

CHAPTER 6

A Dream
Come True

EVER SINCE THE 1890's, when Trevor Kincaid had knocked around Puget Sound with Brooks Randolph in the primitive little *Maud*, he had been aware that on the seashore, that narrow strip of land spread out between the limits of the high and the low tides, was the whole plan and design of life on earth.

Here the superb story of evolution was dramatically revealed in all its grandeur, beginning with the one-celled plants and animals that are so small that a teaspoon can hold a million dancing, twisting specks of life. From this simple beginning each succeeding group became more and more complex until the seashore drama ends with the huge whale and other vertebrates, each group merging gradually into the next in a glorious fulfillment of a master plan, yet each retaining characteristics of its own.

Kincaid was almost intoxicated with the variety, the color, and the beauty of the seashore world that lay at Seattle's doorstep, and of which most people knew so little. On his first acquaintance with the seashore he had sworn that some day he would organize a laboratory where students could broaden their vision of life on the universe by studying the tremendous number of living forms found at the edge of the sea.

The idea of setting up such a laboratory at the University did not originate with Kincaid. In the late 1880's and early 1890's Professor Johnson and the Young Naturalists had cruised around Puget Sound in small boats collecting starfish, clams, sea urchins, and barnacles. But because of the critical, constant shortage of money and equipment for the struggling young school, there was little hope that it could continue to sponsor these field trips. As Professor Johnson's invalidism increased and the Young Naturalists became "Old Naturalists," seashore study in Washington declined, but Kincaid, even when he was a bottle-washer, was determined to keep the idea alive.

Only within the past forty-five or fifty years had scientists in many parts of the world begun to look deeply into the 71% of the earth's surface covered by the seas. In the intervening half-century, investigation of the oceans had increased rapidly. The great *Challenger* Expedition (1872–1876), which had set out from London on an experimental cruise, had brought back the science of oceanography. About the same time, the Scandinavians were busy with tow nets trying to catch living creatures in the plankton and dredging animals off the ocean floor. Anton Dohrn had established a laboratory at Naples for the study of the sea. Louis Agassiz operated a laboratory on Penikese Island off Massachusetts. A few years later the marine laboratory at Woods Hole was established.

Alexander Agassiz made a number of voyages to learn what lay below the coastal waters. A marine laboratory was built at Plymouth, England; Stanford University opened a school for the study of the sea at Pacific Grove in California. The University of Wisconsin had come half-way across the United States to establish a marine base on Vancouver Island; Washington State College had a marine laboratory at Newport on Puget Sound.

Kincaid felt that notwithstanding the strategic position of the state of Washington and the remarkable opportunities it offered for the study of marine problems, "The University is sitting on her hands." He was sure the state must sooner or later become a leader in the investigation of the sea, for in addition to its rich seashore life, Washington had a varied coast line with protected harbors, inland seas, and the restless ocean pounding on her shores.

But who was there, he wondered, to sponsor such an institution? And if organized, where should it be located? There had been mention of Rocky Bay in Kitsap County and Port Townsend. On a brief visit to Friday Harbor with L. M. Gardener, a graduate student in marine algae from Stanford, Kincaid discovered the rich and beautiful fauna of the San Juan Islands. Lying between the northwest coast of Washington and Vancouver Island were more than a hundred islands, large and small, all of them covered with dense forests and ringed with high cliffs or rocky beaches. These islands were to Kincaid the most beautiful blending of land and water he could imagine, and offered limitless fields of investigation and recreation.

He was convinced that this area was what he had been looking for. In his excitement he hurried to President Kane to ask if he would provide him with a boat to look more closely into this wonderful, natural aquarium. Kane agreed, and Kincaid headed straight back to the San Juan Islands. More and more impressed with the beauty and the biological treasures of the San Juan Islands, Kincaid sent reports to President Kane which were filled with superlatives.

Kincaid's accounts of the advantages of the area for the marine station were so convincing that in the fall of 1903 Kane said, "Go ahead and set up your laboratory." But he provided no funds for its operation. Funds or no funds, shelter or no shelter, the very day classes at the University were dismissed, Trevor Kincaid and Theodore Frye, who had never seen the sea before, set out for Friday Harbor with a dozen young students.

Andrew Newhall loaned the group a dilapidated cabin with no window and no door about a mile from the village. They fried their bacon and eggs, steamed their clams, and cooked their sea cucumbers over a beach fire and boiled their coffee in a tin can. Their laboratory was a table under a tree, the dredge a borrowed fisherman's scoop attached to a scow. This they raised and lowered by hand. "But how we reveled in that dredge, for it was always full of animals and we were full of enthusiasm," Kincaid rhapsodized.

By 1906 the budding institution could boast a roof, a floor, four walls, and a door, for an abandoned cannery had been turned over to the dauntless young scientists. Here was shelter from rain and wind, and space for spreading out and mounting specimens. On rainy days a gasoline stove took the place of the beach fire for cooking.

During the first few years Kincaid and Frye attempted no class work; their efforts were devoted almost entirely to the collection and classification of the plants and animals. The species in the waters surrounding the islands were so abundant and so little known that six weeks was scarcely enough time to collect and name them, to say nothing of studying them in depth.

From early morning until dark the little band of students followed the retreating tides, gathering beautiful green, brown, and red seaweeds or prying starfish—ranging from dainty six-rayed species to huge twenty-rayed giants—off the rocks. They also filled their collecting buckets with snails ranging in size from the minute periwinkle to the great moon snail, known as the killer of the beach. Occasionally they spied an octopus hiding under a rock, which upon being disturbed would lash out its eight arms, change color, and swim away. If the scientists succeeded in capturing him, they made octopus chowder from its tentacles. But Kincaid never let the students forget that the real miracle of the seashore was the over-all relationship of the animals and their place in the steady stream of life.

Soon the specter of "no money" threatened the tiny school. In order to save it, the teachers agreed to join forces with Washington State College for the summer, spending three weeks at Olga on Orcas Island and three weeks at Friday Harbor. The experiment was a failure. "The physical difficulty of moving was a nuisance, there were too many straw bosses, and the University was expected to foot all the bills," Kincaid said.

Among the delightful features of the work at the station were the informality that existed between teachers and students, the complete honesty between them, and their dedication to their work. The student-teacher relationship reminded Kincaid of the school run by the Oxford graduate in Peterborough. Kincaid, who had been left to his own initiative there and encouraged to learn from observation and experimentation rather than from class assignments and memory work, now said, "Any fellow who can't dig out information for himself should get a kick in the pants and be set to digging ditches." And certainly the station offered every opportunity for independent work. The material was at hand, and the biological problems it presented were crying to be investigated. But how the eager students longed for reference books and scientific papers to guide them.

In 1909 the cannery in which the marine station had been housed for several years was sold, and prospects of finding other quarters were discouraging until Andrew Newhall again came to its aid by offering the University four acres of land a short distance from the village, provided they would build a suitable laboratory upon it.

During the winter of 1909–1910, Kincaid watched an ugly, two-story, utilitarian frame structure rise on the beach. It contained a couple of research rooms, a laboratory, a lecture hall, and a stock room. For field work a boat called the *Clutha* was acquired. On the hillside high above the beach a far more attractive lounge and combined dining room and kitchen with a huge stone fireplace was built. Along the front was a balcony from which one could look across the water to the ever-changing colors and shadows of Mount Baker and the Cascade Mountains.

For sleeping quarters sixty tents clung precariously to the steep hillside. The boys explained, "We had to brace them against the trees to keep them from sliding down into the bay." A mathematically minded girl estimated she climbed a hundred steps each time she entered her tent. "At least the exercise is good for my figure," she rationalized.

Meals were served at twelve-foot tables covered with oilcloth. Kincaid kept his table mates in high glee with tales of his travels. On Friday nights the students danced to the music of "His Master's Voice," and on Sundays they traveled on the *Clutha* to Orcas or Speiden Island to picnic or to swim in the icy waters of Puget Sound. From these activities many wonderful friendships and a few love affairs developed. Kincaid enjoyed the love affairs only vicariously.

With the construction of a permanent laboratory, classes could be offered in marine zoology, animal ecology, and invertebrate embryology, in general botany, algae, diatoms, and plant physiology. Even with much improved living conditions and a far wider choice of courses, students and professors worked as hard as they had in the days of the tin can coffee pot and the octopus chowder. Kincaid was always the first man at work in the morning and the last to leave the laboratory at night. And certainly there were no bright lights in the village of Friday Harbor to offer competition to work.

Like the University itself, the station continued to have financial ups and downs. In an attempt to balance the budget, Kincaid and Frye invited professors from several midwestern and northwestern colleges to send students to Friday Harbor for the summer. To this end they formed a council composed of representatives of the Universities of Kansas, Nebraska, Iowa, and Idaho, Whitman College, and the Teachers Colleges at Ellensburg and Bellingham with a faculty drawn from these schools. Accompanied by their professors, sixty midwestern students came to the station in 1910, most of them traveling to the West Coast in a private Pullman car.

This plan worked well for several years, but when visitors began to make demands in regard to allocation of funds and selection of teachers, the University of Washington biologists said they could not surrender this authority to the outsiders when the University was providing full operating costs.

By the end of the summer of 1914, differences of opinion within the council of representatives in regard to the operation of the station became bitter, and some of the visiting schools threatened to organize a rival station. During the following winter Kincaid asked to be relieved of regular summer work at the station. His decision may have been motivated in part by his aversion to quarrels and also by plans that were whirling through his active brain. He wanted to see what lay at the next turn of the road and to open up new windows, particularly those within the oyster industry.

When Kincaid left the marine station as its active director, President Kane said, "Kincaid deserves much credit for the tenacity and cheerful optimism with which he pulled the young institution through the first precarious years." The students lamented Kincaid's going, saying "The *Clutha,* the labs, the field trips have lost much of their spirit. There is no one to tell a good story or to make the rafters ring with laughter."

Dr. Frye became the permanent director and a good one. His first important decision was to dissolve the council and to conduct the station solely as a University of Washington project. Nevertheless, it continued to draw students from all parts of the United States and a number of European countries.

During the next decade a definite step forward was taken by the station with the *Publications of the*

A zoology class in the laboratory on the four-acre Marine Station campus. C. T. Frye leaning against a table (center rear). Trevor Kincaid chatting with a student (right rear). The facilities were used until 1923, when the new Puget Sound Biological Station was built.

The Marine Station at Friday Harbor in 1911. The students slept in tents scattered through the woods.

The Violet *taking a class to Olga, Orcas Island, for a morning of dredging about 1917.*

Puget Sound Marine Station, the first permanent outlet for the work of students and teachers dealing with marine problems. Seven volumes of about 400 pages each appeared. The publications were important to the prestige of the station, for an institution, as well as a professor, is often judged by the number of publications it produces.

After Trevor Kincaid retired from active participation in the Biological Station at Friday Harbor, he still returned to the laboratory he loved as often as he could to teach a class, direct a research project, check the progress of an especially promising student, or just for a few days rest.

In the late nineteen tens, Kincaid, Frye, and other scientists realized that although the four-acre campus on the steep hillside had served well for thirteen years, it would not be capable of meeting the needs of the increasing number of students interested in marine problems much longer.

An unused military reservation a couple of miles from Friday Harbor would make an ideal site for a greatly expanded biological laboratory, they believed. (The name of the facility had been changed during World War I from Marine Station to Puget Sound Biological Station.) They enlisted the support of Washington's senators and representatives, who presented the matter to the Department of the Interior. In 1922, by a special act of Congress, the 484-acre military reservation was transferred to the University of Washington. Another of Kincaid's dreams had come true.

About this time fishermen, tourists, and summer-home seekers were flocking to the beautiful San Juan Islands. Fearing that the abundant marine life in the waters surrounding the station would be depleted, the biologists recommended that the state safeguard the animal and plant life of the area by making it a marine preserve. The preserve was set up during the meeting of the next legislature.

Construction of the new station began at once, and by the summer of 1924, unit plan, fireproof laboratories built of hollow stuccoed tile with red tile roofs for general zoology, botany, and invertebrate embryology were almost ready for use. A combined dining hall, social hall, and library were built and a modern kitchen staffed by dietitians and cooks from the University food services was ready for use. Sleeping quarters would still be in tents, as at the old station (minus the hundred steps). Until the finishing touches on the laboratories could be completed, the new station boat, the *Medea*, would run a water taxi service (about a mile) back and forth from the old station to the new so that needed classrooms could be utilized.

Never had the prospects for a successful summer been more promising than they were at the opening of the new facilities in 1924. Dr. Frye had worked hard to provide a gala reception. More than 150 students and research workers were expected to inaugurate the new campus.

Of course, Trevor Kincaid was on hand to celebrate the event. That year Dr. John Guberlet became a regular staff member at the station, where he was to oversee the work in invertebrate embryology. Dr. Harold Kylin of the University of Lund had come from Sweden for the summer to teach marine algae. Dr. Victor Shelford of the University of Illinois was to conduct a class in animal ecology. Professor Leona Sundquist of Bellingham Normal was to give instruction in normal school botany, and

Dr. Brode of Whitman College a course in general zoology.

On the opening morning of the summer school session only a few details remained to be finished. The dining room floor was not all laid, and a few tents were not set up. By the middle of the morning it began to rain, not gentle "liquid sunshine," but a downpour. The noon ferry brought fifty students, who spent the afternoon shivering in their cold tents; the evening ferry carried seventy-five more unhappy scientists. Dinner was served under the dripping fir trees outside the dining room. Rain trickled down everyone's neck. It was cold and there was no place to keep warm. Not even in bed could one be sure of comfort, for many of the tents leaked.

The new students began to grumble. "Not the kind of reception we planned," Frye and Kincaid lamented. "What can we do?" Then Frye had an inspiration. "In the morning why don't you tell these latter-day pioneers about the summer we organized the station? You can make it humorous and shame them into taking minor inconveniences with a smile."

The next morning the newcomers stood glumly around the outdoor tables. There was not a dry spot to be found except in the laboratories and they were not ready for course work. They were very cold and damp. Stoves had no pipes and chairs were few. After a generous breakfast of hot coffee, bowls of steaming Cream of Wheat, bacon, eggs, and rolls taken with a few drops of rain, the students were somewhat happier, however. When their stomachs were full, Professor Kincaid rapped on his coffee cup for attention, and then began to speak:

It is exactly twenty years this month since Dr. Frye and I came to Friday Harbor to organize a marine station. Today you complain about a couple of rainy days and an unfinished hardwood floor. Try to put yourselves in our place in 1904 when our only laboratory was a table under a tree; our only shelter a dilapidated shack with no window and no door. We did our cooking over a beach fire. I assure you we didn't eat roast beef and apple pie prepared by University dietitians as you did last night.

But we had a dredge and the sea was full of strange animals and we knew the sun would shine tomorrow. We were happy as kings and rich as Croesus, not in money, but in hope and ambition. Today the sea is still full of animals and we can still go dredging. Now you go to your tents, put on warm clothes and heavy boots, bring blankets to wrap up in and we will go collecting. Biologists can't be softies and Washingtonians never worry about a little rain.

That was all the young biologists needed. Off they ran to prepare for the field trip. In half an hour they were back, their steps springy, their eyes shining, their faces wreathed in smiles and they carried mountains of blankets. A few small patches of blue could be seen in the sky. Not a member of Guberlet's embryology class or Kincaid's morphology class was missing. Unceremoniously the students climbed onto the *Medea*, perched on overturned collecting tubs or squatted on the deck, talking of a thousand things. The boys of former years staggered onto the boat under the weight of huge coffee and bean pots, hundreds of sandwiches, and skillets for cooking sea cucumbers.

After the *Medea* had traveled for an hour or two, the rain disappeared and the sun broke through the clouds. Everyone relaxed. A few of the girls succeeded in getting suntans and one, a painful sunburn. Professor Kincaid walked to the pilot house and said, "Captain Scribner, let's dredge here at Olga." The captain slowed the engine, and Kincaid said to the students, "The contents of the dredge are as exciting as a grab-bag. What will it contain— sponges, starfish, tunicates or barnacles? Maybe an octopus. You never can tell."

Students of former years cleared the deck aft, and the metal dredge, which was about five feet square and to which a loosely woven fishnet bag was attached, was lowered over the stern of the ship. With the boat moving slowly ahead, the dredge scraped plants and animals off the sea bottom, scooping up everything in its path. After ten or more minutes the ringing of bells indicated that the dredge was full and ready to be raised on the creaking winch. When it reached the level of the ship a conglomeration of seaweed, rocks, clams, pectens, starfish, and sea urchins was dumped onto the deck. The students from the Middle West stared open-mouthed at these offerings.

The more agile animals tried to scamper out of sight, but the slow-moving sea urchins and snails were at the mercy of the students, who dropped them into their collecting buckets. Spying a sea-lily, a dainty highly specialized echinoderm, among the other forms, Professor Guberlet snatched it up and held it high, almost shouting, "O boy, this is only the second sea-lily I've ever found. I'm always on the lookout for them. About like winning the Irish Sweepstakes!" He placed the sea-lily in a bottle as carefully as though it were a precious jewel.

Again and again the dredge was dragged across the floor of Puget Sound. After the second dredge was taken, the new students ventured to pick up a clam or snail. After the fourth dredge they were as eager as the old-timers to collect choice specimens, squealing with delight at a particularly beautiful starfish or shuddering at the sight of a ratfish.

"Save the cucumbers. We will fry them for lunch," said Kincaid, picking up a long red squashy animal covered with tube feet.

"That's a cucumber? It looks like an oversized wiener with the measles," laughed Wayne Wells.

"The only kind of cucumber I am familiar with is the garden variety. But I'm willing to try anything once," remarked Hiram Essex from the University of Illinois.

"At the moment dredging probably seems to you like a huge jigsaw puzzle," said Kincaid, "but by the end of the summer the basic pattern and plan of all life will be clear. You will see that the same principles operate in a starfish, a clam or a man—feeding, eliminating waste, respiration, reproduction." Kincaid's simple, unaffected manner and his clear, direct explanations made everyone want to get to work. Already the students realized there was much work to do, the animals in the sea multitudinous, and the summer session short.

And so it went until noon, when Dr. Guberlet called to Captain Scribner, "If we are going to cook the cucumbers we had better land." Amid much giggling and some consternation, the students transferred from the swaying *Medea* to rowboats and were landed on a gently sloping pebbly beach at East Sound. Under the practiced hand of Clair Hannum and other former students, a beach fire was soon blazing, the muscles of the cucumber cleaned and washed, and the gourmet cucumbers fried in butter. The chefs had more customers than they had bargained for. After a tentative nibble, even the most

squeamish girl admitted the cucumbers "were
pretty good. Almost like oysters."

No dredges were taken on the return trip. Kincaid
and Guberlet decided there had been a sufficient
introduction to the seashore for one day.

When the *Medea* dropped anchor at the station
the students, old and new, were singing at the tops
of their voices:

> Oh, we went to Friday Harbor
> Just to work a little harder
> Singing paddle, paddle, paddle all the way
> The natives shrug and call us bugs
> Singing paddle, paddle all the way
>
> Fare thee well, fare thee well
> Fare thee well old Station float
> For we're off to do collecting
> Just to get a pail of pecten
> Singing paddle, paddle, paddle all the way

The sun was shining brightly and spirits were high
as kites. Summer school in the new, quite sophis-
ticated, Biological Station was off to a good start.

When the gong sounded for dinner that night, everyone was surprised to see that the floor had been
laid; the meal was served at round tables painted
apple green, each set for six. The table conversation
ranged from starfish to politics, from philosophy to
circus clowns. Four-foot logs blazed in the fireplace.
Everyone was gay and happy. The meal over, an
amateur musician sat down at the old upright piano
and played, "Everybody Loves My Baby," "Tea for
Two," and "When My Sugar Walks Down the
Street."

After that first day, occasional showers, roaring
fires in the fireplace, boat trips to neighboring is-

lands, the informality of life at the station molded the students into a closely knit unit. Almost every evening before settling down to studying, a group walked to "heaven" to watch the sun drop behind the Olympic Mountains, rowed to Friday Harbor to buy a magazine or a coke, or played a couple of fast games of ping pong.

Saturday evenings brought a baseball game umpired by Kincaid, who admitted he never could tell the difference between a strike and a ball. Later old and young joined in a masquerade dance with costumes such as a hula skirt made from cold, slimy kelp, or a crown fashioned from a basket starfish. Ingenuity was at a premium. The masks off, they whirled and turned in square dances, and those who were really "with it" danced the Charleston.

Friendships developed quickly between students of various backgrounds. Madeline Pierce, a professor of zoology at Vassar, was somewhat shocked at first by the informality of life at the station, and the students were a little awed by her broad New England accent, but after a few days she forgot her reserve and became the center of fun and merriment. Stina Grippenberg, a chemist from Finland, kept her American friends in gales of laughter with her confusion of terms and her attempts at American slang.

Without doubt, Father Warren Nye was the favorite of everyone from the cooks to the Director— playing baseball, roasting wieners at beach parties, visiting beer parlors. At dances he sat on the side lines vigorously tapping his feet to the music. On Sunday mornings scores of boys and girls, many of whom had probably never attended a Catholic service, drove to the little country parish church to hear him conduct mass.

Tragedy came one Saturday night following a party when half a dozen boys and girls climbed a cliff above the bay to watch the play of the moonlight on the water. As they were returning to the dining room lounge, Eugene Miller slipped on the dry grass and plunged to his death on the rocks below. To his young friends it was a tragic end to the life of a highly intelligent, happy young man.

The spirit of the station was such that it was hard to say where work and play began or left off. Was it work or play when Dr. Guberlet's embryology class stayed in the laboratory all night to study the effect of the full moon upon the spawning habits of the nereis worm, a phenomenon that could be observed only after dark. For weeks prior to that date the class talked of almost nothing but "the night the nereis spawn." On that night these two-inch, many-segmented worms break the bonds of home (a tube in the sand) and swim to the surface for a night of revelry. When the calendar announced that the day of the full moon had arrived, the students scanned the heavens anxiously, for if the moon were shrouded in clouds, the drama would have to be postponed.

But on that August day in 1924, as the great orb of the full moon pulled itself above the horizon, twenty young scientists and their professors gathered on the station dock, armed with flashlights, dip nets, and battery jars. Like worshippers in prayer they knelt at the water's edge waiting for the performers to appear.

"There's a pale green female," said Martin Johnson.

"Another female," squealed Phoebe Blalock. "Where are the males? Aren't they coming to the party?"

Soon the somber gray males appeared, swimming leisurely about. At first the sexes completely ignored one another. But not for long. "Look, the water is becoming white with the sperm," said Martin Johnson.

"And the females are dropping their eggs," added Professor Kincaid. In a few minutes both males and females were dashing through the water in a frenzy of movement, giving off such quantities of sex products that they formed an almost solid curtain of potential life. After half an hour or so of activity the females became listless, all passion spent. One by one they fell back into the water to their deaths. In a short time the males too sank to the depths.

"Too bad they had to die, but their mission in life has been fulfilled, I suppose," said Phoebe.

When the excitement was at its height, the students, following the directions of Kincaid and Guberlet, filled battery jars with water in which were the eggs and sperm of the nereis. They carried the jars into the laboratory and placed the sex-laden water on microscopic slides. Never taking their eyes from the eyepiece, the students soon detected a slight movement on the slide; fertilization had taken place. Within minutes the first cell began to divide into two cells. Kincaid wandered about the laboratory, sat down beside a student a few minutes to explain the wonder of cell development. At a slower rate the two cells divided into four cells, then into eight, and after a couple of hours into sixteen. In order to record the development of each successive stage, the students sketched the tiny creature and noted its changes in their notebooks.

As they watched this miniature creation, a feeling of reverence and awe pervaded the laboratory. For fear of missing a step in the exciting story of the beginning of life, the young students gave their utmost attention to the unfolding drama, not even taking time to eat their sandwiches or drink their coffee. Professor Kincaid said, "Tonight you have come as close to seeing life begin as is vouchsafed to most people. It is a moving experience to observe."

Dr. Guberlet rose from his chair, stretched, and said, "Let's all call it a day. It's almost five o'clock. From this point the development slows down and you can watch it tomorrow. But be sure to be back in the lab at noon to see the next act of the play."

Kincaid and Guberlet trudged up the hill toward their tents to go to bed. The young people, too excited to sleep, finished up the night by rowing out onto the bay to watch the sunrise.

Again the years passed. In December 1930, Dr. Frye tendered his resignation as Director of the Biological Station. Under him the growth of the station had been continuous and successful. With his going a new program was inaugurated. Recognizing the vast marine resources in the San Juan Islands and adjoining ocean areas, the Regents authorized the foundation of the University of Washington Oceanographic Laboratories as a graduate school and appointed Thomas G. Thompson as its director.

Work in many phases of marine study was incorporated into the program. Included were the Puget Sound Biological Station and new laboratories on the University campus open throughout the year to research workers in biological, chemical, and physical fields.

Through the years the primitive institution founded by Trevor Kincaid in 1903 has fulfilled its founder's dream, becoming one of the outstanding institutions in the United States offering a comprehensive study of the seas and bringing the wonder of it all to thousands of young men and women.

CHAPTER 7

Hunting Gypsy Moths in Japan and Russia

A FURTHER OPPORTUNITY for Trevor Kincaid to broaden his view of the world and to open new windows had come in 1906, when he was asked by Dr. L. O. Howard, Chief of the United States Bureau of Entomology, to go to Japan to investigate the life history of the gypsy moth, an insect that was damaging many trees in New England.

Kincaid admitted that he knew almost nothing about the gypsy moth, but as always when challenged, he read everything he could get his hands on about the moth. He found that until recently the gypsy moth had been practically unknown in the United States. Now it was doing considerable damage, and its spread was viewed with alarm.

The moth had been introduced into the country from Germany by a professor who was trying to breed a species of silk worm that could withstand the attacks of enemy insects. While waiting for the eggs to hatch, the enterprising but careless scientist placed a cluster of gypsy moth eggs in a tree and covered them with a canvas. A gust of wind blew the canvas off the tree and scattered the eggs in all directions. The eggs hatched and the population increased in geometric ratio until in a few years they were causing millions of dollars of damage. The pests were carried from locality to locality by the winds, on trains and other conveyances on which the moths laid their eggs. It was feared that should the gypsy moths reach the great forests and orchards of the Pacific Coast, they might, within ten years, cause widespread defoliation that would eventually kill the trees.

When the gypsy moth first appeared in New England, two methods of eradication were proposed: Interaction by parasites, and control by insecticides. Most entomologists, including Kincaid, believed the natural control by parasites to be the better deterrent to the spread of the moth. But species of parasites that were enemies of the gypsy moth were practically non-existent in the United States. It was known that in Japan the gypsy moth was kept under control by parasites, and they had never become a serious problem in that country.

Kincaid received a leave of absence from the University to make the study. He was accompanied to Japan by Jiro Imada, a graduate student, whose family he planned to visit in Tokyo. Later Imada was to act as his interpreter.

As soon as he reached Tokyo, Kincaid got in touch with Dr. Naohide Yatsu, head of the Department of Zoology in the Imperial University, who made arrangements for him to live in a small hotel near the University. The landlady had never entertained a foreigner, and she feared that an American would be hard to please. Kincaid hastened to assure her that he wished to be treated just as she treated her other guests. His simple, unaffected manner and his sincerity soon won her over, and they got along famously. She found he could be as polite and bow as low as any good Japanese.

At first he was puzzled by such customs as leaving his shoes at the house entrance, sitting crosslegged on a cushion on the floor, eating with chopsticks, and by the ubiquity of rice and tea. But after a few weeks these customs seemed perfectly natural to him. When he could pick up peas with the chopsticks without fumbling, he knew his Japanese table etiquette was acceptable.

The strange young American did sometimes scandalize the household by calling the maid and pleading, "O Nesan, sumi, motto okure kudasai," which meant "Oh, honorable daughter of the household, come carrying charcoal, please." Then he would buy a nickel's worth of fuel. After a five-month stay in Japan, Kincaid, with the help of his remarkable memory and his diligence, learned to speak the language passably well.

On his first trip to a moth-infested forest, he observed that the gypsy moths laid their eggs on the bark of trees in clusters containing 350–500 minute specks. To protect them against the cold of the winter, the female mother covered the clusters with a soft fluff from the under side of her abdomen.

The eggs were just hatching when Kincaid arrived in Japan, which gave him the opportunity to observe the entire life cycle of the moth. He examined many species of parasites of the gypsy moth, but he found a species new to science which, at his request, was named in honor of a Japanese scientist, *Schedius kuwanae*. *Schedius kuwanae* (now called *Coencyrtus kuwanae*), a parasitic wasp, was the most effective control. The eggs of the parasite were laid singly in the moth and hatched there. The larva matures by destroying the nutriment within the moth egg, leaving only the husk, thus preventing the development of the moth egg.

Eventually the parasite emerges as a fully formed but very tiny adult insect. Both the moth egg and the parasite egg are microscopic. The life cycle is completed in approximately three weeks. This parasite was the answer to the spread of the gypsy moth in the United States, Kincaid believed, so he gathered large numbers of parasites and sent them to the Highlands Melrose Laboratory near Boston for testing and propagation. To prevent the hatching of the eggs before they reached their destination, the egg clusters were removed from the bark of the trees with a knife and arranged in cases, which were placed in the cold storage compartment of a ship bound for Vancouver; from the ship they would be hurried to the Highlands Melrose Laboratory, where, it was hoped, the parasites would develop. The plan was that when they reached the adult stage they would be broadcast into the woods, where their eggs would destroy the gypsy moth eggs.

Although *Coencyrtus kuwanae* has proved the most effective and widely recognized enemy of the gypsy moth, at best only about 55% of the moth eggs were destroyed. By 1929, twenty years after the parasite had been introduced into the United States, it was estimated that 574,000 parasitic wasps had been released into the infected areas and that parasites had reached almost half the gypsy moth eggs. Under the most favorable conditions, there was naturally a high element of chance as to whether every egg would be penetrated by the parasitic wasp. In fact, the ravages of the gypsy moth have never been entirely checked. Even in 1974 it remains a formidable shade and fruit tree pest in Northeast North America, and it has appeared in California.

Before shipping the parasites to the United States, Kincaid had to make sure that they were not infected with other species of parasites. If they were, the secondary parasites might nullify the work of the first and thus create greater problems than the gypsy moth had. Sometimes parasites were infected with tertiary parasites. Another problem he had to consider was whether the parasite might not become a pest itself. With the assurance that none of these fears seemed justified, Kincaid felt it would be safe to broadcast the tiny animal through the New England woods.

As he pondered the destruction of the gypsy moth egg by a microscopic parasite, Kincaid was always conscious of the complex workings of nature. Would the whole story of the actions and interactions of living matter ever be fully understood, he wondered.

Japan, however, was not all work for Kincaid. He met many zoologists who entertained him elaborately. At a party in his honor six beautiful geisha girls danced for his pleasure. He drank sake and tea with fellow faculty men. He banqueted on exotic foods with the Mikado's scientists. Only the necessity of making a trip in pursuit of a colony of gypsy moths prevented him from accepting an invitation to call on the Empress. At the Marine Station, the quarters of the Crown Prince, a highly trained zoologist, were turned over to the young Westerner, and two servants ministered to his personal needs. As Trevor worked in the Crown Prince's quarters, his thoughts ran back over the ten years since he had arrived at the University of Washington with his boxes of insects in borrowed carts. Yes, the years had opened many windows to his world.

At Hiroshima and at Sendai, he observed methods of oyster culture. Years later, when Japanese oysters were introduced into the state of Washington, seed oysters (spat) were imported from these oyster beds on a large scale under Kincaid's direction.

During his search for the gypsy moth parasite he visited all parts of Japan. One of the delights of his visit was following the spring as it moved northward. On island after island, from Kyushu in the south to Hokkaido in the north, in the cities of Tokyo and Kyoto, the streets were crowded with gaily dressed women, their costumes almost as colorful as the blossoms. In Kyoto the famous *miyako-odori* or cherry blossom dances were presented by 700 geisha girls.

The great curving highway that borders the Sumida River in Tokyo was lined with cherry trees whose branches intertwined overhead. To Kincaid the effect was like passing through a silver tunnel many miles in length. Sunrise from the top of Mount Fuji was also spectacular, but unquestionably the most moving experience, and one that showed the Japanese people's almost worshipful love of flowers, was a glorious unfolding of morning glories in a park in Tokyo just at sunrise.

Several hours before dawn Kincaid joined large numbers of men, women, and children assembled in an amphitheater to wait for the sun to appear above the horizon. At the bottom of the bowl, countless pots of morning glories were banked, each of which had been trimmed down to produce but one or two blossoms of unusual size. When Kincaid arrived at the park, the flowers were still tightly closed. All he could see was an immense blanket of dark green foliage.

As the sun rose and its warm rays poured down upon the plants, the concentration of the men and women became intense. Then almost as if by magic, the flowers burst open until a great mass of blue the color of the heavens spread across the amphitheater. Up to this moment there had been absolute silence among the spectators. But as the flowers opened, a gasp and a sigh of contentment and thanksgiving arose from the crowd.

The decorative arts of Japan impressed Kincaid almost as much as did the scientific efficiency of the people. As he wandered around Japan, he gathered a variety of artistic objects, including one hundred representations of frogs. A local artists' group, hearing of Kincaid's collection, asked to see it. Seated on the floor in his rooms, the young craftsmen looked at the frogs, which ranged in size from an inch in diameter to six inches or more. As a check against his own appraisal of his *objets d'art,* he asked the artists to indicate his best piece. They chose an inkwell in the form of a frog to be used in making seal impressions. Carved in cedar, it was fashioned with the fewest possible strokes of a knife. "One more stroke would have been superfluous, one less would have spoiled the effect," the leader of the group said.

To Trevor Kincaid, Japan was a land of mystery, beauty, charm, and industrious people, and it was hard to leave it. For years after returning home, he exhibited the frogs and gave talks on them and on other forms of Japanese art.

The Government officials who had selected Kincaid for this project were enthusiastic in their praise of his work. The 1908 *Alumnus* reported: "Both as a scientist and as a gentleman he was a worthy representative of the United States."

The year after Kincaid's trip to Japan to study the gypsy moth scourge, where he had proved to be tireless in tracking down the natural enemies of the pest,

Dr. Howard asked him to go to the interior of Russia to continue the search.

Kincaid was not eager to visit the cold, forbidding country. Still he felt it would be ingratitude to refuse the request of Howard, after benefiting for years from his friendship. So he set out for Russia, going first to Washington, D.C. to talk with Howard and to obtain his credentials to enter Russia. Then he went to the Highlands Melrose Laboratory in Boston, where he learned that the parasites he had sent home from Japan had been released into the forests of New England and that hopes were high that they could prevent further spread of the gypsy moth.

Kincaid traveled by ship to France and from there took the Nord Express for the long, bleak journey across France and Poland to St. Petersburg (later called first Petrograd and then Leningrad). He watched the monotonous countryside glide past. Birch trees were the only living things to break the sameness of the landscape. Even in May the sky was leaden and patches of snow lay in sheltered places. Men dressed in sheepskin jackets and felt boots plowed the fields for spring planting, while barefoot women trudged along the muddy, rutty roads to and from log hut villages, their bodies swathed in dull black garments, their backs bent from carrying heavy burdens.

As the train drew into St. Petersburg, the city Peter the Great had built on the marshes by the Gulf of Finland, Kincaid saw on the station platform hundreds of Cossacks, their black astrakhan hats cocked jauntily on their heads, their long black coats reaching nearly to the ground, and dozens of women who resembled nothing so much as shapeless bundles of clothing.

Stepping into the street, Kincaid looked down the

handsome Nevsky Prospect, at the end of which stood an immense statue of Peter the Great watching over his fabulous city. He was also greeted on his arrival by the thundering roar of the "breaking of the waters" as the Neva River ice fought to free itself from its winter prison, and by the sight of pontoon bridges linked by great chains being floated back into place.

While waiting for his credentials to be checked and learning which were the best areas in which to study the gypsy moths, Kincaid, with a German Baedeker in his hand and a hazy knowledge of the peculiar letters of the Cyrillic alphabet in his head, set out to see the city. Everywhere were statues of czars and generals on horseback. Bridges, canals, and palaces were massive and impressive.

The Hermitage, with its priceless paintings and great sculptures of solid gold, many of them plundered by Catherine the Great's armies from the ancient Greek cities on the Black Sea, was beautiful beyond anything Kincaid had ever known. He missed nothing, even making a visit to the baths that guaranteed a cure for rheumatism. (He was simply curious.) In his *Autobiography,* he concluded his comments upon St. Petersburg by stating nonchalantly, "I was rather glad to get away from there, since I found an epidemic of cholera was raging, causing many deaths."

He left the cholera-ridden city and took the train for Odessa, where the real search for the gypsy moth parasites was to begin. Across the tundra and pine forests of the north, through the wheat fields of the Ukraine, to the oak forests bordering the Black Sea, he traveled, storing in his mind hundreds of impressions of this vast, complex country.

In Odessa he sought out the American consul to ask his help in finding an interpreter and assistant. The consul recommended a Russian- and German-speaking Jewish boy who could understand a little English. In his halting German, Kincaid explained his plans. The young man shook his head and gesticulated, "Nichts zu kaufen, nichts zu verkaufen. Was fur ein Geschat" (Nothing to buy, nothing to sell, what a funny sort of business).

Finding no parasites in Odessa, Kincaid went to Bessarabia. There the peasants were mostly Roumanian, and few of them could speak Russian, much less English!

Here my Russian interpreter was not much use, for he could not speak Roumanian. So I had to find a second interpreter who could speak Russian and Roumanian. I formulated the question in English, put it to the Russian. He put it to the Roumanian, who passed it on to the Roumanian workmen, who neither knew nor cared about the gypsy moths or their parasites. Then the answer came back through Roumanian, into Russian, and finally into English. The results had little relation to the original question. It was like a game of Post Office we played as kids.

The next most likely place to procure moths, Kincaid was told, was at Ganchesty, the capital of Bessarabia. There were no hotels or boarding houses in Ganchesty, so the Governor made arrangements for him to make his headquarters on an estate belonging to a Russian nobleman, which was close to an oak forest said to be heavily infested with the gypsy moth. On the day set for Kincaid's departure an immense carriage drawn by four horses drew up in front of the hotel.

The first part of the drive to the estate was over a fine macadamized road, but when the carriage en-

tered a side road, the highway became rutted and
muddy, ending in a squalid village where water was
drawn from a well by a sweep, pigs rooted in the
mud, and the inhabitants were dressed in rags.

In contrast to the filthy village, the nobleman's
castle to which Kincaid had been directed was richly
furnished with priceless paintings, objects of art, and
a well-stocked library. Although the castle was kept
in immaculate condition, it was used by the owners,
who lived in Paris, only when they entertained
friends.

Behind the castle were a number of handsome
villas, where the manager and other important personnel who looked after the vineyards, farms, and
forests lived. Kincaid was assigned to one of these
villas. An impromptu laboratory was set up back of
a barn for his use.

Life on the estate and the methods of farming used
by the peasants were so unusual that Kincaid's mind
was sometimes distracted from gypsy moth parasites.
When help was needed in weeding a wheat field, the
manager sent a call to the peasants of the village to
be at the gate at nine o'clock in the morning. With
the workers came a five-piece band. To the accompaniment of rollicking tunes, laborers formed a long
line and swept down the field, weeding as they went.
Coming to the end of a row, they wheeled, keeping
time to the music, and came back in the other direction. This routine was continued until noon.

In the meantime a fire had been lighted in the
middle of a field and an immense pot of borscht prepared. When this hearty dish was ready to be eaten,
Kincaid joined the workers, who, laughing and talking, dipped thick slices of black bread into small
troughs into which the food had been poured, and

feasted. To top off the mid-day merriment old and young threw down their shovels and hoes and danced.

After he had spent a month and a half in the neighborhood of Ganchesty without finding any new parasites, he went to Bendery, where conditions were almost identical with those in Ganchesty. Again Kincaid moved on, this time to Kiev. He was becoming discouraged. The hotels were uncomfortable and the food poor. Yet he continued his search. Perhaps the next woods would yield the elusive species he was seeking.

As he was unpacking his valise in Kiev, the landlady dashed into the room in a state of great agitation, pouring forth a flood of Russian words. What had happened? Was the house on fire? Had some great tragedy occurred? Close behind the woman came Kincaid's interpreter. Pointing to an ikon on the wall, he gasped, "You whistled in the presence of an ikon."

"This is forbidden?" asked Kincaid innocently.

"If you do that, some tragedy will befall the household."

Kincaid was abject in his apologies.

"Since I was ignorant of the god's aversion to whistling, maybe we can persuade them to spare the household from tragedy. Won't you pray for its deliverance?"

"I don't really believe the superstition myself," the boy admitted, "but why take chances? And is it more foolish than your superstition of the number thirteen?"

In Kiev, the center of religious life in Russia, were sixty-five churches. The ecclesiastical system was centered in the Lavra, an immense monastery which accommodated seven hundred priests. Beneath the

Lavra were extensive catacombs. Kincaid and his interpreter purchased candles and joined a group of pilgrims for a tour of these subterranean passages. A fat priest with a bunch of keys dangling from his rope belt unlocked heavy iron doors and let the worshippers down endless corridors.

Seated on benches in the alcoves along the corridors were figures draped in red cloth, the remains of priests. The peasants stopped before each glass-covered alcove, crossed themselves and kissed the glass. Kincaid's reaction to this act was not one of devotion; to him it meant only the spread of disease. Although to Trevor Kincaid the Russian church appeared to be saturated with superstition and graft, he found the singing of Gregorian chants by a choir of fifty bearded monks an inspiration.

On and on he went, searching for that one species of gypsy moth parasite that would wipe out the damage done to the foliage of trees by the moth. When he tried to make arrangements to have a number of parasites sent back to the United States, he found that the shipping of live insects out of Russia and across Germany entailed much tangled red tape. In the end, the lack of care given the specimens resulted in the death of most of them before they left Russia.

The Russian expedition was on the whole disappointing, yielding little new information on the control of the moth. But it had given Kincaid an opportunity to survey the gypsy moth problem over much of this vast country. He had also seen the unrest, the poverty, and the inequalities of life in Russia, and he foresaw the coming of some sort of national upheaval. Through his close observation of detail his knowledge of peoples and countries was greatly expanded.

Realizing he would not be able to track down new parasites, he decided to return home. Since at his back he always heard "Time's wingéd chariot hurrying near," and knowing he would in all probability never visit Russia again, he traveled on, obsessed with the idea that he must see everything that came his way.

After he crossed the Black Sea, he arrived in Constantinople (Istanbul), where he was more impressed with the dog population in the city than he was with the Mosque of Santa Sophia. At the time, Constantinople was said to harbor more dogs to the block than any city in the world. Kincaid counted sixty in going a couple of blocks to the Post Office. A single dog somewhere nearby would start to howl, stimulating all the dogs in the neighborhood to bark until it sounded as if every canine in the universe were yelping at the top of its voice. The Young Turks, who had recently overthrown the old regime, had in the last year decided to get rid of the dogs, a scourge they considered almost as menacing as the despotic rulers. Their method of ridding the city of dogs was to dump them by the hundreds into the sea.

From Constantinople, Kincaid went to Smyrna (Izmir), Athens, and Naples, where he visited the marine laboratory situated on the beautiful Bay of Naples, the oldest center for oceanographic study. From Naples, Kincaid hurried on to London and Scotland, where one last adventure lay ahead—seeing the place where his family had its roots.

Since the days when Trevor had driven with his doctor father through the Canadian countryside to visit his patients, the lad had listened to stories of his father's youth in Ireland and the long history of the family in Campsie, Scotland. Now he was seeing this ancient homeland. Wandering through the ancestral grounds at Campsie, he examined the foundations of the original tower built in 1280 for protection against warring clans.

The present Kincaid house, which had been built in 1820, was impressive and austere. At the time of Trevor's visit, the heir to the estate, Major John Kincaid, did not make his home in Kincaid House, for he had married the daughter of the Duke of Lennox and was living in Lennox Castle. Kincaid House had been turned over to relatives, but because of the remoteness of the relationship, Trevor did not feel justified in calling upon them. (Since World War II, crushing British taxes have necessitated the sale of Kincaid House to the government. It was converted to a guest house for tourists, and Lennox Castle became a state institution for mental defectives.)

But Trevor Kincaid, steeped in family lore, wandered through the ancient churchyard at Campsie, read the names upon the vaults, and mused before the individual grave markers, each with the coat of arms on which was the motto, "I will defend." Then he traveled to Donegal, Ireland, remembering the tales his father had told of his youth there. As he approached the village square, suddenly one of these scenes came to life.

Sitting on a low bench were a number of elderly women selling bags of dulse, a kind of edible seaweed. They might well have been the same shawl-draped women his father had known fifty years earlier. Out of sentiment Trevor bought a bag of dulse and carried it to his father thousands of miles across the seas. Also, out of sentiment, he had the hearthstone of the farmhouse where his father was born dug up and shipped to Seattle, where it became part of the hearth in his study.

But this nostalgic journey too must end. His odyssey was over. Pride in his clan had been intensified, for only a family rooted in loyalty, industry, and good works can survive through seven hundred years. With one last look he imprinted in his mind the meadow where his father had tended the cows, watched the sea, and dreamed of what lay beyond. Trevor Kincaid turned his thoughts toward his own home. In Cork he took a steamer for New York and from there went directly to Seattle.

CHAPTER 8

A Public
Servant

AS THE POPULATION of Washington grew, as high schools became standardized, and as Seattle boomed, the enrollment at the University increased each year by 15 percent. By the end of President Kane's administration, the enrollment had reached 2,381, while the number of accredited high schools rose from 45 in 1902 to 126 in 1913. Once more there was a critical shortage of classrooms at the University.

No new buildings had been erected since 1902, when Science Hall was constructed. Yet very soon after its completion the freshman chemistry class was so large that it had to meet in the auditorium of Denny Hall. Chairs in the Library numbered 100, when 250 were needed. The shortage of accommodations became more and more acute. Kincaid said that the crowded conditions haunted President Kane.

He warned the Regents in 1907 that if more space were not provided, it would be impossible to start the term. At long last the lawmakers acknowledged the need for additional classrooms, but before the legislature convened and the matter of buildings was acted upon, an event occurred that changed the campus and affected the University for years to come.

A committee of Seattle businessmen, who were conscious of Washington's remoteness from the mainstream of life in the United States, proposed that a big fair to be called the Alaska-Yukon-Pacific Exposition be held in Seattle in 1909 to boost the state and the city. The University of Washington campus was considered the ideal site for the fair because of adequate space and the fine view it offered of Lake Washington and Mount Rainier.

Edmond Meany, who was both a trustee and member of the Fair Committee, presented the idea to the Regents. The legislature approved the plan and appropriated $1,000,000 for the Exposition, $600,000 to be used for an auditorium, a pharmacy-chemistry building, and an engineering hall, as well as a heating plant, shops, and a foundry. Three hundred thousand dollars was earmarked for modernization of the campus.

But the University could not wait two years for buildings. In a desperate attempt to relieve the shortage of space, small temporary buildings were thrown up everywhere. In December 1908, half-finished classrooms in the engineering and chemistry buildings and in the basement of the auditorium were forced into use, but improvising went on as before until every nook and corner in the campus had its desk or rostrum.

The orgy of construction—hammering, rumble of trucks, and the clatter of paving—was so deafening and the blasting so violent that President Kane feared the existing buildings would collapse.

To Trevor Kincaid the most far-reaching evidence of the impending exposition was the pushing back of the wilderness on which the University stood. This beautiful piece of land stretching along Lake Washington was quickly transformed from a dense wood filled with native plants—salal, Oregon grape, ferns, and huckleberry—to an open slope of more than a hundred acres laid out in formal gardens, walks, pools, and fountains with a central vista looking toward Mount Rainier.

Kincaid looked with horror as the trees, the trails and thickets that had provided excellent examples of the harmonious relationship between plants and animals (including Meany's arboretum) were destroyed overnight by tractors, shovels, and hatchets. He knew the loss of the natural environment was something that could never be restored.

While the plans for the exposition were being completed, Kincaid went to Russia to continue his study of the gypsy moth. He returned a few days before the Fair closed to learn that 4,000,000 persons had passed through the turnstiles and that the event was pronounced a huge success.

Kincaid spent a week or more viewing the exhibits and talking with Edmond Meany and other colleagues about the effect of the exposition on the building program. They all agreed that it would postpone the use of the permanent buildings for a couple of years and that when available they would require extensive repairs and changes. And so it proved.

Then the question arose as to the wisdom of pressing into service the buildings that had been put up solely for the duration of the fair. Kincaid felt this would be short-sighted economy. The folly of this policy was evident when the Forestry Building, which during the fair had featured Washington's magnificent forests and the important place lumbering held in the state, was torn down. It was by far the most impressive building erected for the exposition.

For its construction, hundreds of the giants of the forest had been cut. The buildings was archaic Greek in style—312 feet long, 128 feet wide, and 98 feet high. One hundred twenty-eight Douglas fir columns, 42 feet long, 4 to 6 feet in diameter, and weighing 25 tons each, supported the building. In all, 2,016,000 feet of logs and 30,000 shingles were used in its construction. Samples of woods and other forest products were displayed in the building, as well as fruits, grains, grasses, wild flowers, fishes, and entomological collections.

From the day Kincaid had first seen the plans for the building, he had envisioned it as a future museum in which to display the extensive collections made by the Young Naturalists and other early-day scientists. Open galleries extended the length of the building, lighting was adequate, and storage space ample. Immediately after the fair, to Kincaid's great delight, the building became known as the Washington State Museum.

In the next few years the museum made remarkable progress, both in quality of displays, in financial support, and in numbers of visitors. But it soon became evident that Kincaid's hope for it was not to be fulfilled. The logs began to shrink; spaces between them permitted so much vibration that the exhibits were disarranged; dust from the bark drifted into the cases; the roof leaked; and the foundation needed to be reinforced. The building was drafty beyond imagining, and Arctic conditions prevailed in offices and exhibition rooms.

When the bark began to peel off the columns through the work of wood-boring beetles, Kincaid as well as architects and engineers realized the beautiful building was doomed. No amount of renovation could save it. In 1925 it was closed to the public and torn down soon afterward.

Had the materials been properly seasoned and the building adequately constructed, Kincaid said, it could have remained a monument to the superb forests of Washington for a century and provided a worthy home for the University's collections.

Attempts were made to save other temporary buildings to help meet the building shortage. According to Dean Frederick Bolton's unpublished history of the University, "Several departments were delayed in securing proper quarters one or two decades because it was mistakenly assumed that the A. Y. P. had donated such generous housing to the University. Of the temporary buildings only the Washington State Building and the Lumberman's building served the University for any length of time."

Everyone agreed that the highly developed, formalized campus was beautiful, but it did not exemplify the Northwest. Kincaid said that the last vestiges of the natural growth disappeared when a narrow strip of trees and shrubs along the north edge of the campus which had been saved was cut down to provide a parking lot.

To keep the campus in first-class condition after the Fair and to save expense, Edmond Meany sponsored a Campus Day each spring with tree planting, speeches, maypole dances, and a May Queen, which came to be one of the gala events of the school year. Students and faculty donned old clothes (even the Governor was relieved of his necktie), wielded spades and shovels, repaired tennis courts, and built tees on the golf course. This tradition was kept alive for twenty years.

Following Kincaid's return from Russia and the severing of regular summer ties with the Marine Station, the direction of his activities changed drastically. Although he spent almost eighteen hours at the University each day, and his study of insects and fresh water plankton was as painstaking as ever, he rarely published the results of his investigations. He became an information bureau to the curious public. His reputation as a man of encyclopedic knowledge grew until by telephone, by mail, and in person requests came to him for information on all manner of subjects.

Patiently and courteously he attempted to answer all questions. Many of them no one could have answered. For instance, "Caruso, my pet canary, is suffering from a severe sore throat. What do you suggest for a gargle?" or "My gold fish has parasites. Shall I fumigate?"

Answering one phone call, he was greeted with a conglomeration of warbles, twitters, and peeps. The woman at the other end of the phone insisted they were the exact reproduction of the song of a bird she had heard in her back yard. "Tell me the name of the bird," she demanded.

"The sounds reminded me of nothing so much as static," Kincaid said to himself.

Probably the most baffling request came from a religious group, which was expecting the end of the world momentarily. Their enterprising leader asked Kincaid where the tallest trees grew in Washington. His followers wished to be ready at the first sign of calamity to climb the trees in order to have a head start in their flight to heaven.

A woman wrote a letter listing 27 questions about the coddling moth. "To answer the questions would have required a whole quarter of research work. I recommended she take an extension course in entomology," was Kincaid's comment.

When a woman asked, "What is the best age to marry?" Kincaid was stumped. "Since I have never married, you had better ask someone more experienced in the matter of matrimony," he answered.

He talked to the ladies of the Elderbloom Club; accompanied groups of Girl Scouts on beach walks; gave a series of lectures to the Teamsters' Union (one of the most rewarding experiences he ever had); and appeared as a lecturer at teas given by fashionable women's clubs.

He had a vivid recollection of a trip to Bremerton on a cold, snowy night to present an illustrated lecture on the "Home Life of the Bee." Although he was suffering from a severe cold, he took the streetcar from the University to the ferry terminal. Arriving an hour later in Bremerton, he found no one to meet him, so, carrying a projector and a box of lantern slides, he trudged a mile or more through slush and snow to the lecture hall.

Before Kincaid was called upon to speak, much time was consumed with club business—the reading of the minutes, thank-you's to this and that committee; discussions of what refreshments to serve at the next meeting; who would be in charge of the table decorations.

At the conclusion of Kincaid's lecture, the audience gave him a standing vote of thanks. He nibbled at the cake and cookies, was introduced to dozens of Bremerton matrons, and answered numerous questions about the care and keeping of bees. As he was leaving the hall, the chairman accompanied him to the door and said, "We want to pay your ferry fare." Meticulously, he counted out seventy-three cents for the round trip ticket.

Alone and on foot, the professor, weighed down with his impedimenta, found his way back to the ferry. He just missed the midnight streetcar to the University District. The cold kept him in bed for the next week.

Kincaid was also in great demand for travel talks on the then rarely visited places of the world he had seen. Men's service clubs and church groups booked him months in advance of the dates of their meetings.

Like the early-day Methodist preachers, the willing lecturer was often recompensed for his services in apples, smoked salmon, bouquets of flowers, and on one occasion by a large pumpkin. "Just in time for Thanksgiving pies," he joked.

Kincaid also served as expert witness in cases involving disputes between paper mills and the oyster farmers. As a result of his suggestions, the paper mills made a number of changes in the control of their waste materials. He made regular surveys of the fouling of the beaches, and traveled across the state to inspect blight on peach orchards.

All of these extra-curricular duties he did for the love of the state and as a service to its citizens. He was one of those rare faculty members who felt he was a public servant, and if people wanted answers to their questions, it was his duty as well as his pleasure, to supply them from his vast fund of information.

By this time Kincaid had become a legend on the campus. Practically every student at least knew his name, had heard his favorite jokes, and was eager to catch the spirit of the man behind his public facade. Students from many departments came to his classes.

Especially was his course in evolution popular. Three hundred students registered in it in 1916, a time when the subject of evolution was extremely controversial in the United States, as the Bryan-Scopes trial a few years later proved.

One serious young man, on registering for the class, announced that he didn't believe in evolution, "But I decided to take the course to see what arguments you would concoct in its favor." The doubting student attended class regularly, listened attentively, took notes carefully, and passed a good final examination. However, in a P.S. on his paper, he wrote, "You put up a good bluff, but I don't believe a word you say. You will have to find better arguments to convince me that a man and a monkey are brothers."

The discussion of evolution naturally led to the professor's being asked about his religious beliefs. He answered as objectively and scientifically as possible, saying, "The beautiful, natural world unspoiled by man is my cathedral and the divine laws of nature my God; the daily rising and setting of the sun, the regular passage of the seasons, the eternal rise and fall of the tides, the endless progression of the stars in their paths, prove that such perfect coordination of nature's laws could not have been achieved without a master plan behind it."

Yet, he added, "To me, the idea of a life after death, or of a soul, is contrary to facts. If a man has a soul how did it originate? Was it in the sperm, in the ovum, in the fertilized egg, in the embryo, in the gastrula, or in the squalling infant when born? From whence did a soul come?"

Then he went on to explain that over millions of years, through a complex evolutionary process from the anthropoid, man has been derived. Did the anthropoid have a soul when it emerged? How can one localize it? Has the soul ever communicated with the living?"

"Then what is the meaning of life?" challenged the inquisitor.

"That is an enigma for which no final answer can be given. We find ourselves as sentient beings upon a tiny sphere in the midst of a boundless universe. We know there was a time some five billion years or more ago when the world did not exist as we know it. It was during this time that the great evolutionary plan was being fashioned. We know too that in some future time a lifeless earth will revolve around a dying sun. Even now, man has discovered means by which human life on this planet can be terminated almost instantly if he so desires.

"My suggestion, therefore, is to live each day to the fullest, to make our world a better and happier place for our having sojourned on it for a little while, and to say with Robert Browning 'wait death, nor be afraid.' Charles Darwin, when asked the same question, answered, 'The safest conclusion seems to be that the whole subject is beyond the scope of man's intellect.' "

Then Kincaid added, "As I look at the myriad stars among which our earth is a tiny mote, I realize the entire cosmos from the giant sun to a single atom of hydrogen is ruled by universal chemophysical laws. I am brought face to face with the God of the scientist, awe-inspiring, inscrutable."

"But don't you believe in the church?" came the next question.

"Of course I do. The church performs a very valuable function in society and is perhaps man's finest institution. The progress of civilization has stemmed largely from it." In this way, Kincaid, the scientist-philosopher, clarified for many a thoughtful man his concept of the world and its meaning today.

Driven by the rush of events and the hurrying years, Kincaid found that he could not investigate in detail each scientific problem that came to him. It was also the pressure of time that made him decide that for the present teaching and service to the public were of greater value than were his writings.

Some of Kincaid's colleagues, commenting on the middle years of his life, felt he gave too much time to the trivial requests of people, thereby dissipating his own remarkable talents. They believed that for the sake of his lasting reputation as a scientist, he would have made a greater contribution to knowledge if he had let a lesser man serve the public, while he recorded the results of his endless studies. These criticisms were probably valid.

Although the students sometimes laughed at him or with him, the laughter never stemmed from derision but from enjoyment of his unique personality, his humanity and quick wit. Most important, his name was always spoken with respect. *The Columns,* a campus humor magazine, bestowed the leather medal upon Kincaid for being the faculty member with the best sense of humor.

His dry humor was spontaneous, according to a young co-ed whom Kincaid admired very much, and who he said was the most beautiful girl he had ever seen. She said that one afternoon, as she and the professor were watching the graduates in their academic gowns assembling before marching into the Auditorium, she asked, "What kind of gowns do the M. A.'s wear?" Quick as a flash, he answered, "Mother Hubbards."

A graduate assistant reading Kincaid's lecture notes, which through the years had become soiled and dog-eared, found in the margins of his notebook reminders to himself, such as "Tell the clam joke here." This joke was based on the fact that certain species of snails bore holes into the umbo of a clam, then suck the juicy body of the clam through the hole. After a pause in the lecture, the professor would stop a moment, scratch his head, and say, as though the idea had just occurred to him, "I suppose that is a case of being bored to death." Year after year the students laughed at this joke, not so much because it was funny, but because Kincaid enjoyed it so much himself, his laughter booming out above the entire class.

It could truly be said of Trevor Kincaid, "The man who loves to laugh, loves life." Certainly no man connected with the University loved life more than he did, and the years did not silence his laughter or dim his zest for living.

CHAPTER 9

The Good Angel of the Clean-Up Squad

IT MAY HAVE BEEN the emotional stresses of World
War I or it may have been the question put to him
recently—"What is the best age to marry?"—that set
Kincaid to thinking about marriage in relation to
himself. He had never shown much interest in
"women." He sometimes walked home with a student who had worked late in the laboratory or took
a friend to the movies. It was rumored that he would
have liked to become more than a casual friend to a
couple of co-eds. However, the girls discouraged
closer friendships, no doubt because of his age, his
devotion to his work, his careless dress, and his family
responsibilities.

In any case, Trevor Kincaid now began to weigh
the advantages and disadvantages of marriage and to
look at the girls more closely. In the end he concluded as Charles Darwin had done, "My God, it is
intolerable to think of spending one's whole life like
a neuter bee, working, working with nothing after
all." Thus, in the fall of 1914 when a tall, slender girl
with shy charm and dignity walked into his entomology class, she caught the professor's attention.
"I must find out about her," he thought. Was she
taking the course because she was interested in en-

tomology or to fulfill a science requirement? He did not ask himself if she wanted to meet the well-known eligible professor.

Whatever the reason for taking the course, it was Louise Pennell's introduction to science, and it opened a new world of thought to her. As an English major she was steeped in Chaucer and Shakespeare. Now she became fascinated with the study of moths and butterflies and the intricacies of evolution. Louise Pennell was also enrolled in a class in public speaking. The speech instructor had assigned a talk on a subject of the student's own choosing for the following class period. At a loss to know what to talk about, Louise asked the entomology professor to suggest a topic. Busy as he was, Trevor dropped everything and rushed home to get Lafcadio Hearn's delightful story about singing insects, with which he had become acquainted in Japan. "The first night I had the cricket, I hung the bamboo cage in my room, but during the night it sang so loudly I had to take it out into the courtyard," he told her. Hearn's story also appealed to Louise because, as a young girl in Florence, Italy, where her father was studying voice, she had watched children putting crickets into bamboo cages to hear them sing.

When the next quarter opened, the girl with the soft voice and gentle manner was registered in another zoology class. Kincaid now noticed other things about her—her serene gray eyes, sweet smile, calm brow, smooth brown hair. In the lecture room she sat next to George Bailey, the blind ringer of the chimes, that had recently been given to the University by Alden Blethen. In order to help Bailey with his class notes, Louise learned Braille, an act of thoughtfulness that told Kincaid much about her character. Soon he realized he had more than a teacher's interest in her.

With the completion of this course, she took another and then another course in biology, until by the end of the school year of 1915 she was graduated with a major in zoology. Prior to this time she had not thought of doing graduate work. Now the professor assured her that if she wished to enroll for a master's degree, he could give her a job as laboratory assistant in the department at fifteen dollars a month. This was too good an offer to turn down. She could continue to see her favorite professor, and the fifteen dollars would help her extremely limited budget.

For years Kincaid had been an ardent photographer, and many early-day events at the University were preserved and recorded in his snapshots. He had recently photographed the several hundred students in his evolution class. Naturally, he needed assistance in developing and printing this prodigious number of pictures. And who would be a better helper than his laboratory assistant?

When the films were developed and printed, the darkroom was in a shambles. Louise helped him clean it up. The dirty job took almost a week to finish. In the confusion of the photographic darkroom, the supposedly confirmed bachelor fell in love with Louise Pennell, twenty years his junior. Yet he dared not speak to her of love. The only way he knew of thanking her for her help and of expressing his love was to give her a box of chocolates with the message, "To the good angel of the clean-up squad."

A few days after he sent her the chocolates, Trevor went to Olympia to try to build up the native oyster industry, which, because of careless methods of cultivation and harvesting, was threatened with extinction. He knew the box of candy was not enough to convince her of his love, and he was tortured with the thought that she would never care for a man who was lost in scientific pursuits and who had no social graces. In spite of his doubts he wrote and asked her to marry him.

The young girl, reared by a strict New England mother, tried during the next few days to think of this unusual man from every possible angle. His complicated family, the disparity in their ages, his habit of working in the laboratory until midnight, his frequent trips to far countries to study baffling biological problems—these might make for a difficult marriage. To offset these shortcomings she remembered his gentleness, his unpretentiousness, his innate goodness, his humor, his service to all who sought his help, his unusual mind. And certainly he was the first man who had seriously attracted her.

Louise was in an agony of uncertainty. She loved her Professor. How should she answer him? She wrote and tore up half a dozen replies. Finally she suggested they let the matter rest for a year. If at the end of that time they both wished it, they would talk about marriage.

Trevor accepted her decision gratefully. It was much more encouraging than he had dared hope for. For another year Louise worked side by side with him preparing laboratory materials, overseeing students' work, running the lantern for his lectures, and confirming her impressions of his character and habits.

Sometimes on a Friday night Kincaid donned his best suit, probably badly wrinkled, brushed his wayward hair, put on a necktie, and took his "good friend" via streetcar to a string recital or a voice concert at the Moore Theatre. Stopping at Rogers University District restaurant for a dish of ice cream on the way home was a high point of the evening. From a worldly point of view, Louise realized Kincaid was neither a "Gibson Model" nor a wealthy man, but she was sure he would become a distinguished scientist, and his personal character and his desire to serve his fellow man completely overshadowed any other consideration.

Finally spring arrived, and Louise was to take the oral examination for her master's degree. The examination was conducted by Dr. Frye, Dr. Osterud, and Kincaid in Kincaid's office. When she entered the room the bashful lover unloaded a dozen books and papers from a rocking-chair and suggested she sit down and be comfortable. But she would have no pampering. She sat in a straight chair facing her inquisitors and answered their questions in a clear voice. The other two men on the committee should not suspect there was anything "between" her and the professor. As was to be expected, she passed the examination with high praise from the committee.

The year of waiting was over. The master's degree had been bestowed, and Trevor Kincaid was more determined than ever to put a wedding ring on her finger. Thus, with the excitement of war settling upon the United States, Louise Pennell and Trevor Kincaid, on August 23, 1917, were married at noon in the Plymouth Congregational Church, of which she was an active member. A story his wife did not deny was that on his wedding day Trevor had to be hustled out of his laboratory and told to hurry or he would be late for the ceremony.

Apparently he reached the church on time, but the service was delayed almost an hour because the bride and groom had decided that water lilies would make a beautiful bouquet. The florist was having difficulty locating water lilies that morning and wanted to substitute roses, but water lilies it must be, because Trevor liked them and they were indigenous to the area. The Reverend Doctor H. H. Gowen performed the ceremony in the presence of dozens of University friends. Louise's father gave her away and her sister served as bridesmaid. The bride never could remember what food was served at the Y.W.C.A. for the wedding breakfast. All she knew was that it was the most beautiful wedding ever celebrated and she the most fortunate bride.

The newlyweds went to Paradise Inn on Mount Rainier for a week's stay. They had a beautiful time hiking along the trails, looking under stones for insects, chasing butterflies with Trevor's ever-present bug net, and taking photographs of wild flowers and of each other.

A honeymoon would not have been complete to Trevor without a visit to the Biological Station at Friday Harbor. With the abandon of children on a picnic, the bride and groom put-putted through the San Juan Islands in his tiny motorboat, the *Ha Ha*. Wearing a skirt that reached her ankles and a hat securely tied on with a scarf, Louise hopped in and out of the boat to get a better view of a starfish-strewn beach, snail-covered rocks, or a bed of purple sea urchins.

At dusk they headed for the station, moored the boat at the dock, and prepared their "tea for two" in kettles designed to hold food for dozens of students.

They slept on mattresses piled high in the middle of the dining room. (Summer school had closed, and no one was at the station but the caretaker.) The night they arrived he invited the newlyweds for dinner in the kitchen. The next morning they returned the courtesy by asking him to share their bacon and eggs.

Louise was blissfully happy. And for Trevor, married life was all he hoped for. In a letter to Dr. D'Arcy Thompson he wrote, "On August 23, 1917 the most important event of my life occurred." Yet Louise had thought of this man as "her professor" for so long she could not bring herself to call him "Trevor" until two months after they were married.

As she had realized she would do before her marriage, she moved into Trevor's home on Brooklyn Avenue with his mother, who was now almost blind and severely crippled with rheumatism, and his sister Airdrie. Fortunately Louise had been brought up to be a thrifty and expert housekeeper and although the household arrangements and her mother-in-law were often difficult and the finances limited, all that really mattered was that she and Trevor loved and understood one another.

Kincaid's friends at the University wondered whether this shy, young girl would be able to stop the flood of stories about his absentmindedness and his irregular habits of work. Only time would tell. One of her first encounters with her husband's absentmindedness involved her hat. One morning as he was leaving for the University, he could not find his cap, a very special one he had worn for years. It was raining and he needed a head covering, "so he laid claim to his wife's coquettish little toque." Louise pleaded, "Don't wear it; you will cause a sensation." The zoologist cared little for sensations. Across the campus he paraded, all decked out in a hat with a feather projecting from the brim. In defense of his hat he said, "The Scotch wear feathers in their hats, and this is just a little thing made from part of a Navajo blanket."

Stories of Kincaid's idiosyncrasies continued to circulate. One of these was that one morning just after he had left for the University, Louise walked into the bedroom and saw his trousers draped over the back of a chair. In consternation she thought, "He couldn't have gone off without them." She threw a coat around her shoulders and with the trousers tucked carefully under her arm, she rushed down the street after him. Along the way she inquired of several persons if they had seen him. Yes, he had passed them, but they did not seem concerned. On she ran, catching up with him just as he entered the campus.

"What is all the hurry about?" he asked.

"But Trevor, your trousers were hanging over the back of a chair."

"My new suit has two pairs of pants. I'm not that absent-minded," he scoffed and walked on.

Marriage did not greatly change Trevor's way of life, although following his marriage, his travels to far countries completely stopped. In the more than fifty years after his return from Russia, he never left the shores of the United States. As he had done for years, he walked briskly from his home on Brooklyn Avenue to old Science Hall for an eight o'clock class, his hat perched on the back of his head, his coat flying. In his pocket he carried a cyanide bottle into which he popped any unwary ant or beetle lurking along the path.

To keep her husband well groomed and looking "like a professor," his young wife cut his hair in a short crew cut. Each Monday morning he set off with his clothes carefully pressed, a crease down the front of his trousers. By Tuesday the crease was beginning to disappear. By Thursday the bottoms of the pants were usually wrinkled from mud puddles he had stepped into while snaring unusual specimens.

It was reported that on occasion he wore one black shoe and one brown one. (If one shoe was overly muddy, he chose another, not necessarily a mate to the original pair.) His explanation for his change of appearance as the week wore on was, "I never know when or where I will find an interesting specimen, so I gather everything along the way, sometimes at the expense of my clothes." Louise watched this change in his appearance with regret, but she never harassed him by trying to change him.

When the classes for the day were over, he took the cyanide bottle from his pocket and transferred the specimens to the microscope. If there was something new or particularly interesting in the day's collection, he spent the evening dissecting and classifying it. Louise early learned the meaning of the term "laboratory widow."

There was no telling when he would arrive home for dinner, and the family often ate without him. This did not upset Louise, for she knew her professor had been doing something more interesting to him than eating. (Food had always been of minor importance to him.) When she heard his step on the walk she quickly prepared a bowl of oyster soup, a serving of cottage cheese, and a banana, or an equally sparing meal, but one which usually included a product of the sea. She sat beside him while he ate, talking of the affairs of the day. At the end of the meal his comment always was, "Thank you, my dear. That was a fine dinner."

A couple of years after the Kincaids' marriage, they had their first child, Marjorie Farrar. There was never a father more proud and delighted with a baby than was Trevor, Louise said. When this dainty little girl, a small replica of her mother, could call him "Daddy," he remarked, "She is the most interesting and beautiful specimen I have ever been able to study." In quick succession two more daughters were born, Dorothy Elizabeth and Barbara Louise. Then came the family's only son, Thomas Farrar. When he was born, Trevor, thinking of the care he had given his parents, said to Louise, "Now we have a son who will look after us in our old age." Later two more daughters were born, Mary Pennell and Kathleen.

Some of his friends at the University joked, "Trevor must be trying to see if the Mendelian Law actually holds true." When asked about his big family, he chuckled and answered, "It is getting hard to keep track of them. I am thinking of making a card file."

Louise, reminiscing later on the early years of their marriage, said, "Trevor loved the babies passionately, cuddling them to his breast, the warmth of their tiny bodies lighting his heart and soul." When they were older, with a child on each knee he would rock back and forth in an heirloom rocker and read *Mrs. Quack, Billy Goat's Gruff,* and many other children's book.

But as the children grew older, their father became shy of them, not knowing quite how to communicate with them. He taught them to make collections of minerals and rocks, to mount butterflies, to catch insects and to preserve them. He told them stories of starfish and clams. In time, however, the children came to look upon this kindly man more as a teacher—a very indulgent one—than a father. Was the age span between the generations too great to be bridged?

Trevor's doctor father, who had taken little responsibility for his family for years, was now failing rapidly. A friend in Olympia wrote, "You had better come and get your father. He should not be alone here." Kincaid hurried to Olympia and brought the once handsome, imperious man, who had practised medicine there for thirty years, to Seattle. He was emaciated and unshaven, his hair long and unkempt, his mind partially gone. His mother, now completely invalided by arthritis, and his father bickered as of yore. For two years Trevor cared for his father as though he were a child. Shortly before his death, the doctor admitted, "Trevor is a good boy." Both Dr. and Mrs. Kincaid died in 1923.

Through good times and bad, Trevor's home remained a haven for any member of the family who needed either financial help or a temporary refuge. His sister Airdrie, who had lived with them for several years, married and moved to California. Zoe, who had gone to Japan while Trevor was there, married a British newspaperman and lived in the Orient for many years, but returned to Trevor's home when the United States went to war with Japan. Her husband was a prisoner of war and died in captivity soon afterward. His brothers Morden and Kenneth dropped in for longer or shorter stays. His devotion to his family was deep and fervent.

The old house on Brooklyn Avenue was getting too small for the burgeoning Kincaid household. The University District was growing rapidly, and with it the demand for business property, so Trevor sold his house for an apartment house site. The Kincaids then built a large home on the corner of Northeast 52nd Street and 19th Avenue, Northeast, in the heart of the residential section of the University District, a most convenient location for a growing family of children with diversified interests.

After her husband's death, Mrs. Pennell, Louise's mother, came to make her home with the Kincaids, taking over much of the responsibility of the children's upbringing. In his *Autobiography,* Trevor commented, "Discipline of the children rested with their mother and their Puritanical grandmother, and I am inclined to think they did a good job." Sometimes though, Mrs. Pennell's determination to bring up the children exactly as she had been reared in Massachusetts fifty years before created some problems.

The girls wore long black stockings and high-topped shoes long after their friends were shod in brown-and-white oxfords and white socks. Their dresses came well below their knees. They had to perform certain household tasks and practise their music lessons, and they were severely chided for any breach in table manners. Even on Christmas morning, breakfast had to be eaten, dishes washed, beds made, and the house tidied before they could as much as peek at what Santa had brought them.

Faithfully the children attended Sunday School and morning services at the Plymouth Congregational Church, where they sat primly between their mother and "Nanna," who nudged them gently if they whispered or coughed. When very young they were taught to join in the reading of the Scriptures and the singing of hymns.

In the early years of his marriage, Trevor accompanied the family to church because Mrs. Kincaid said it set a good example to the children. Trevor was fundamentally a religious man, but remembering his own unhappy experiences as a child with an overdose of church attendance, he sometimes remonstrated with his wife on the subject, arguing that the children would be in God's temple whenever they walked on a sun-drenched beach or sat by a quiet stream. "To seek God through nature" was his religion. He believed that, alone in wonder amid the solitudes of nature, no one can but feel there is more to man than the mere breath of his body.

After several years of rather spasmodic church attendance, he quite often managed to have an important speech to prepare on Sunday morning or he said he could not understand the indistinct enunciation of the minister. "Perhaps my hearing is getting bad," he rationalized. (Fortunately the differences in their religious thinking never became an issue between the Kincaids.)

It is possible that Kincaid was becoming restless for wider vistas than Seattle and the local scenes offered. But with wife and children, he knew he must find windows to open closer to home. No longer could he travel to Russia or Japan. Perhaps an automobile would be a means of escape, at least to the mountains and the seashore.

Late one evening a University colleague delivered a second-hand Ford at his door. After a few verbal instructions on its operation, the caller departed, leaving the Kincaids somewhat bewildered. Immediately after breakfast the next morning, Louise called "Come on Trevor, let's go for a ride in our new car." Kincaid, who knew nothing about engines or mechanics, spun the crank of the starter. Louise put her foot on the brake. "Careful, don't run over me," he shouted above the whirr of the engine. In he jumped. "Now what do we do?"

Louise removed her foot. The car began to move. "How do we stop it? How do we back it?" they asked themselves in consternation. For a few minutes they went forward a few feet. Then they went backward. They stopped and they started. Now they were ready to drive around the block. Around and around they went. The next morning Trevor drove to the campus, which was a real test of driving skill, for even in the 1920's there was much traffic on University Way. He drove in "low" all the way to Science Hall (a technique he followed for years).

One evening a few weeks later, Trevor, his mind occupied with his next morning's classes, started home. As he approached the garage he saw that the door was open and the garage empty. He ran into his house and called the police to report the car had been stolen. When he told Louise of its disappearance, she asked, "How did you get home?"

"I drove," he answered.

When the ridiculous situation dawned upon them, they burst into gales of laughter.

For several weeks they played with their new toy. Then they were ready for an adventure, a drive to Samish Bay, south of Bellingham, to visit the oyster beds, which had recently been planted with Japanese oysters.

CHAPTER **10**

Father of the
Oyster Industry

NATURALLY KINCAID WAS curious to see whether the
Regents would succeed in finding the superman
whom they were seeking to succeed President Kane
as head of the University, but either they were not
able to discover a man with all the qualifications they
sought, or the applicants were suspicious of the political interference at the University. In any case it was
not until 1915 that the Regents announced that
Henry Suzzallo, Professor of Philosophy of Education
at Columbia University, had accepted the position.

Although the appointment was hailed with enthusiasm, and hopes were high for his administration,
the new president soon became aware of the faction-
alism and distrust among various elements in the
state. He quickly moved to harmonize the groups by
traveling to all parts of Washington to speak. In his
lectures he emphasized the achievements of the University and the bright future that lay ahead for it.

Professor Kincaid said that Suzzallo was an unusually well-informed man, whose command of English
was spellbinding and who, in spite of a somewhat
rasping voice, charmed his audiences. He became so
popular that soon almost every town and village in
the state invited him to speak to them. His slogan
became "The University of a Thousand Years," a

watchword that lighted a spark of fire in his audiences.

For a couple of years the University enjoyed a period of quiet. But construction could not keep pace with enrollment. No new buildings had been built since 1909, the year of the AYP Exposition. To accommodate the heavy enrollment in home economics and business administration, buildings to house these schools were authorized during the temporary presidency of Henry Landes; their actual construction became Suzzallo's responsibility. Built in Gothic style, the new buildings were very beautiful, although many people believed this type of architecture unsuited to the American West.

During the next year or two Philosophy Hall and the education building were constructed according to the same design. When finished they formed a handsome quadrangle, which transformed the middle campus into an imposing complex. About the same time Horace C. Henry, a Seattle capitalist, gave an art museum, and many scholarships and gifts came to the University.

With the completion of the quadrangle, President Suzzallo began to dream of a library commensurate in beauty with the recently constructed buildings. He believed that because a library represented the collective mind of man, it should serve the entire school and should symbolize the unity and inspiration of man's quest for learning. He believed, too, that a library built to resemble a Gothic cathedral would lift the spirit as well as the mind and give strength and inspiration to all who entered it.

Thus, a beautiful cathedral-like building came to stand on the highest point of the campus. The exterior was richly ornamented with the figures and

the names of great men of history. It very soon
became apparent, however, to Kincaid and other
faculty men that as a working library, it was quite
impractical, and through the years several additions
have been made to it. Today, it is still called the
Suzzallo Library and is the most impressive structure
on the campus.

The President then sent Charles W. Smith, the
librarian, to Europe to buy badly needed scholarly
books. He returned to Seattle with eight complete
sets totaling 5,000 volumes. These books and many
new periodicals did much to strengthen the library
facilities. By 1926 the library's collection numbered
190,000 volumes and its annual budget was $90,000.

Suzzallo also did much to improve the position of
the faculty. He initiated special programs of teaching
and research; promoted the organization of a faculty
research society; shared some executive authority
with his colleagues; appointed faculty men on state-
wide committees; and gave them a voice in the appointment of personnel. Deans and heads of
departments took their proper place in the University. "Their work is creative and cannot be compelled," the President pointed out repeatedly.

World War I brought many changes to the campus,
including a drop in enrollment of 30 percent as 1,500
faculty and students entered military service. The
President himself, appointed State Chairman of Civil
Defense, devoted a great deal of time and energy to
nonacademic activities. For his skillful handling of
the IWW agitation he received much praise.

Roland Hartley, a lumberman with large timber
holdings, was elected Governor. At once he began
attacking Suzzallo, charging him with extravagance,
citing as examples his $18,000 salary and the million-

dollar library. Kincaid believed the Governor's antagonism to Suzzallo stemmed from Suzzallo's popularity in the state and especially from his recommendation during the war that loggers and sawmill workers be granted an eight-hour day, adequate pay, and other considerations.

As the battle between Hartley and Suzzallo became increasingly bitter, the faculty trembled. Soon it became evident that political warfare was inevitable. The final clash came when Hartley vetoed the University budget, and it was passed over his veto. Hartley immediately appointed a new Board of Regents, and on December 1, 1926, Suzzallo was dismissed as President. The situation, quite naturally, had a demoralizing effect upon the University and aroused much debate throughout the state.

In spite of Suzzallo's humiliation, he counseled the students to go back to their studies and the faculty to stand by the University. He also urged new faculty men to follow the plan Kincaid had always used when things were in a mess—to find a challenging piece of research and to retire to their laboratories or offices with it.

Although many of Suzzallo's friends supported him and formed an organization to recall Hartley, no action came of it. Everyone acknowledged Suzzallo's brilliance and his intellect, but he had few staunch supporters who went "all out" for him, even among the faculty. Some thought him distant and somewhat domineering. Kincaid said, "My reaction to him was that while he did not become intimate with members of the faculty, his formality was due to his desire to treat everyone on terms of equality. He was always most friendly to me and was the only President to call me by my first name. Certainly he was not the kind of man who could go down to the Faculty Club and play pool with the boys."

Charles Gates, in his history of the University, said that Suzzallo's dream had been to lay the foundations for the "University of a Thousand Years," but like Kane he had done little more than lay a firm plank or two. One important tenet in his philosophy was that a University was not the shadow of one man, but the image of a community of scholars. Although Suzzallo succeeded in leaving a very large shadow on the University, the state may not have been ready for a Suzzallo. Yet, Kincaid said, "The University of a Thousand Years" has remained its slogan.

After the dismissal of President Suzzallo, Trevor Kincaid retreated once more into his laboratory with his books and his microscope, hoping to become an ichthyologist, an authority on fish, planning thereby to increase wartime consumption of this valuable food. He realized that his knowledge of fish culture was meager. Through the years he had collected a large number of local species but they were unnamed. Thinking he could save time by sending them to a specialist for identification, he shipped a dozen kegs of fish preserved in formaldehyde to Dr. Gilbert at Stanford University. Somehow by accident, Kincaid's specimens became absorbed in the Stanford collection, which left him with a numbered series of fish but no specimens.

His only recourse was to take the four-volume set of *Fisheries of North America* by Jordan and Everman and set to work identifying them himself. After months of incredibly hard work, he was able to give all the essential data on the fishes—the family, the genus, and species names, the main features of their life histories, their aquatic range, and their commercial uses, if any. Some years later, under the auspices of the State Department of Fisheries, the hard-working professor published an illustrated guide to the *Pisces* of the North Pacific Ocean.

Kincaid next turned his attention to a long study of oysters. He had never forgotten the wonderful flavor of the oysters he had eaten when he first came to Olympia. In those early days the teen-aged boy frequently accompanied his father on visits to patients in logging camps and fishing villages. While the doctor prescribed pills and "aqua pura" to the ailing men and women, Trevor watched the Indians gather and prepare the small native oyster, *Ostrea lurida*. Even as a boy he realized the Indians were inefficient, unsanitary, and wasteful in their care of this important bivalve. But these shortcomings did not bother him much, for he always managed to carry home enough oysters for a meal or two.

During the intervening years, lack of conservation and unrestricted harvesting made the native oysters almost extinct. In 1911 and 1916 Kincaid had been called to Olympia by the United States Bureau of Fisheries to see what could be done to save the diminishing crop. Thousands of acres of oyster beds had been abandoned. Kincaid's conclusion was that the chances of preserving the local oyster on a commercial basis were very slight.

The native oysters had a delicious flavor and were suitable for soups and frying, but they were very small; 2,000 to 2,500 were needed to make a gallon of opened meats. They were also expensive and difficult to raise because they had to be protected from the heat of summer and the cold of winter by about six inches of water retained in a system of trenches. In addition, the shells were hard to open.

Oystermen from Olympia had attempted to introduce Eastern oysters into Washington waters by bringing in carloads of spat and spreading them on the tide flats of Willapa Bay; but for reasons difficult to explain, Eastern oysters had not thrived in the West.

By 1917 oyster fanciers in the state began demanding a larger species suitable for more uses. When Kincaid visited Japan a decade before, he found that several species were being cultivated there with success. An oyster widely used was *Ostrea gigas,* a form so large that 80 to 100 made a gallon of meat. This species had been transplanted from Hokkaido, a northern province, to Sendai, a hundred miles north of Tokyo. "Transplanting"—that might be the answer to Washington's oyster problems, Kincaid decided. In talking to oystermen about ways to restore the oyster industry on the West Coast, he suggested they think about importing this species of oyster.

But before the Americans did anything about securing the *Ostrea gigas,* two young Japanese, J. Emy Tsukimoto and Joe Miyago, who had grown up in Olympia and had worked on the oyster beds there, began dreaming of organizing an oyster company. With the cooperation of Dr. D. H. Seno, an oyster biologist, the young men checked temperatures, salinity of the water, and food supplies in Puget Sound.

After long and careful study the young Japanese bought 600 acres of tidelands and, joined by eight Japanese businessmen, formed the Pearl Oyster Company on Samish Bay, ten miles south of Bellingham. The next spring they imported four hundred cases of *Ostrea gigas,* a case holding about two bushels or 10,000 to 15,000 oysters, and hurried them to

Samish for planting. The young men had bought mature stock, thinking they would survive the two-week journey on the deck of a ship better than would young oysters.

With the arrival of that ship the Japanese oyster industry was born in Washington. But to their chagrin, Tsukimoto and Miyago found that many of the oysters were dead. Was their ambitious venture doomed to failure? In hopes that a few might have survived, they scattered them on the tide-flats. Examining the beds a few months later, they found that attached to the larger dead oysters were hundreds of very active, almost microscopic, seed oysters called spat.

After this discovery, the young men decided to import only spat. They were cheaper, took up less room on the ship and the scowing from Seattle to Samish was much easier. To their surprise the young entrepreneurs found that the Japanese oysters grew so rapidly in American waters that within two years they had reached the remarkable length of six inches.

However, the Pearl Oyster Company ran into trouble, when, as early as 1918, antagonism toward the Japanese people began to be felt on the West Coast of the United States. In 1922 the owners were faced with the Alien Land Bill, which clouded the title of the company, and made it almost impossible for them to borrow money or to sell stock in the company. The prejudice became so strong that the company, unable to dispose of its oysters, was forced to go out of business.

E. W. Steele, who had experimented with oysters near Olympia for a number of years, became interested in buying the Pearl Oyster Company. He and an associate, Mr. Barnes, visited the Samish beds several times and eventually bought the company, changing the name to the Rockpoint Company.

During the next summer Professor and Mrs. Kincaid, driving their recently acquired Ford, visited this new company. The first question Mr. Steele asked Kincaid was, "Why don't the oysters spawn in our waters?" "Why, indeed? Let's find out," he answered.

In order to make use of the experience of the former owners, Kincaid suggested to Steele that they send Emy Tsukimoto to Japan to supervise the buying and shipping of the oyster spat to the United States. This he did. For their long journey across the Pacific, Tsukimoto placed the baby oysters in cases, flooded them with water, piled the cases on the deck of the *President McKinley* and covered them with Japanese matting. Several times during the sixteen-day voyage, he poured water over the matting.

When the ship arrived in Seattle, the oysters were inspected by customs officers and then taken to Samish Bay. "Thus the young Japanese oysters became immigrants," wrote Mr. Steele in his book, *The Immigrant Oyster.* "One little oyster said to another, 'I believe we are going to like it here.' " And they did. At once the word "Japanese" was dropped in referring to the oysters and the word "Pacific" was used instead.

At the end of his first visit to the Rockpoint Company, Kincaid said, "I have had a lot of fun and I believe I can pull some tricks from my bag to explain the reluctance of the oysters to become Americanized." Already the eager researcher knew that the study of oysters offered him the most challenging project he had yet undertaken, and he spent two more summers working with the Rockpoint Company. Whether to work or to play, the Kincaids loved to visit the seashore. The strange mixture of sound and silence, the lapping of the waves against the shore, the sigh of the wind in the trees, the distant mountains always moved the deeply sensitive man, and he had to follow their beckonings.

The question of the oyster's reluctance to spawn in Washington waters haunted Kincaid, and he worked endless hours on the problem. Was the water too cold? Too deep in the beds? Lacking in essential chemical properties? Being poisoned by wastes poured into the Bay? No one could say.

He also tried to find ways to combat the enemies of oysters—starfish, drilling snails, slipper snails. Kincaid's active brain would not let him rest until he had pursued every facet of this new challenge. Giving attention to the smallest detail, he traced the life history of the oysters from the instant the eggs and sperm were released into the water until they were ready for market. Mr. Steele, commenting upon Kincaid's study of the oyster, said that he brought books, microscopes, bottles, and slides from the University. "We had talks on every part of the oyster's anatomy and on the plankton, its principal food. What a genius Kincaid was. He could rattle off the names of hundreds of almost invisible whirling creatures in the water, names I could neither spell nor pronounce." Steele felt almost desperate at his own ignorance of science.

Up to this time, Steele said, the workmen on the beds had known nothing about oysters and cared less, except that their jobs depended on them. But under Kincaid's guidance they became as excited about oyster culture as they would have been over the unraveling of a mystery story.

An important day in the development of the oyster industry was May 21, 1923. Steele, Kincaid, and several other men were standing on a float near which adult oysters were growing. It was a very hot day, and the water had been warmed as it came in over the pebbly beach, just covering the oysters.

Suddenly Kincaid shouted, "They are spawning! They are spawning! This proves it. The sunshine and the warm water have made them spawn. Temperature is the answer to the puzzle." Pointing to a stringy white substance oozing from the oysters, he continued, "It's the sperm of the males. Just wait a minute."

As he spoke, another substance began to spread over the water until it became white as milk. "Watch," he ordered, "the females are releasing their eggs. The sperm of the males, when mixed with the water that runs over the females, causes them to discharge their eggs. By some inherited instinct the sperm is drawn to the eggs and fertilization takes place."

Then he joked, "Since the oyster Romeo cannot directly approach his Juliet, the business of lovemaking is somewhat complicated. Because both are doomed to sit on a piece of shell all their lives, the oyster Romeo, instead of serenading his lady love, broadcasts his sex products in her direction and hopes."

It is within the range of possibility, he added seriously, that a single oyster might deposit 120,000,000 eggs in one season. Yet in order to maintain nature's balance only a few are fertilized and still fewer mature. Many of the others are swallowed by microscopic animals in the plankton or are destroyed by natural enemies or by the weather.

A short time after the eggs were fertilized on that hot sunny day, Steele and the workmen peered into Kincaid's microscope to watch the division of the first cell. Soon the minute larva divided into two cells, then into four, eight, sixteen, and on and on. With each change they became more active. In a couple of days they developed cilia, hair-like processes, which allowed them to move about. As they whirled across the field of vision in the microscope, they looked to Mr. Steele like ballet dancers. And well they might dance, for their freedom lasted but two or three weeks.

At the end of the free swimming period, the young oysters instinctively sought attachment to a rock or a bit of shell. Nature provides each tiny animal with a spot of adhesive for this purpose. In order to provide anchorage for the oysters, the workmen hurriedly built a cultch, a series of wires that hung into the water. To the wires they attached pieces of oyster shell to which they hoped the minute swimming creatures would fasten themselves.

After the oyster larvae became attached, they grew rapidly and were soon visible to the naked eye. By the time winter set in, they were large enough to survive the storms of winter. By the next spring, if all went well, the young oysters would be the size of a man's fingernail and could safely be removed from the cultch and spread on tide-flats.

Here they were left for a year. By the end of the second year, the once microscopic oysters had grown into clusters which had to be broken up. For a third and last time, the workmen separated the clusters and spread the shellfish on the beds. There they were left until they were of marketable size, usually when they were two or three years old.

With the solving of the baffling question of their natural spawning, Kincaid began a forty-year love affair with the Pacific oysters. So influential did he become in the development of the oysters in Washington waters that he was called "the father of the industry." And no doubt it is his work with oysters upon which his lasting fame will rest.

The Rockpoint Oyster Company had a splendid growth, producing enough oysters annually during the next ten years to more than fill a "cocktail glass taller than the Northern Life Tower."

Spurred by the success of the Rockpoint Oyster Company, Gerald T. Mogan, a capitalist and promoter who had dabbled in many commodities, sought out Kincaid and asked him to suggest likely beds for growing Pacific oysters. Kincaid knew that in pioneer days Willapa Bay, a large inlet from the ocean near the south boundary of Washington, had been the seat of extensive oyster growing, but that the beds had all been abandoned. Not a bushel of oysters had been harvested there in years.

He recommended these lands to Mr. Mogan, saying he considered Willapa Bay the finest location in the world for raising oysters. Mr. Mogan promptly bought 7,000 acres of tideland for taxes, organized the Willapoint Oyster Company, and asked Kincaid to serve as his biological advisor.

At first Kincaid hesitated, thinking of his innumerable duties at the University and, perhaps, remembering his father's unfortunate business ventures. As an incentive for Kincaid to undertake the work, Mr. Mogan gave him forty-three acres of oyster land, which through purchase he increased by ten acres. And for a number of years Emy Tsukimoto made trips to Japan to purchase oyster spat, out of gratitude furnishing seed for Kincaid's acreage.

Following Mr. Mogan's example, other prospective growers began buying tidelands in the Bay until all available acres were under cultivation. The next year, Mr. Mogan, eager to provide every encouragement for Kincaid's work, built a laboratory at Nahcotta, a village near Willapa Bay, and the scientist went to work in earnest. After unremitting toil during the summer, he was firmly convinced that the temperature of the water was the determining factor in oyster spawning, for he had observed over and over that if the water reached 68 to 70 degrees Fahrenheit, a good spawning could be expected.

Unfortunately, the water in Willapa Bay and on most tidelands in Washington rarely reaches that temperature or maintains it long enough to induce oysters to give off their sex products. Yet Kincaid's tests showed that if the water was warm at the time of spawning, the free-swimming larvae were able to survive a later lowering of the temperature to 60 degrees.

Since he could do nothing about the temperature, he hoped that the oysters might become acclimated to the cold water, or that certain beds could be found in which the waters would be warmed regularly to the required temperature by the prevailing winds and exposure to sunlight. Only time would tell.

In the meantime he tried to create artificial conditions for spawning. He built a cement tank 4 X 8 feet and connected it by a pipeline to the bay to provide the egg-laden oysters with a constant flow of water that had been warmed by the sun. He also experimented with a "clair," a heated swimming pool used extensively in France in which the oysters were nursed until they gave off their sex products. But he found that the "clair" offered no advantages over importing the seed from Japan, because it was expensive to operate and difficult to construct. He finally concluded, "Mother Nature's method is far simpler and more efficient than mine. It's pretty hard to improve on that 'old gal.' " The best answer to a supply of spat continued to be importation of spat.

By endlessly watching the habits of the oysters and the weather, Kincaid was able several times to predict three weeks in advance and to within forty-eight hours a heavy natural "set" of oysters. The growers were thus enabled to get the cultch into the beds in time to receive microscopic spat. He also observed that the oysters developed more quickly in the south end of the bay than in the north. The plankton, on the other hand, was more abundant in the north, where it was brought in from the rich "pastures" of the open sea. For this reason he suggested that the growers use the warmer enclosed waters for propagation and then move the oysters north for fattening. As a reserve supply of oysters, the State Department of Fisheries took over 10,000 acres of tidelands in Willapa Bay in case of failure in less protected areas.

Another problem that claimed much of Kincaid's attention was studying the moving waters to make sure they contained sufficient plankton to provide a balanced diet for the oysters. Until this time Mr. Mogan and his workmen had given little thought to the oyster's food. But as they peered through Kincaid's microscope, they saw that the water was laden with millions of twisting, turning, dancing diatoms, microscopic algae, worm larvae, free-swimming barnacles, and other tiny organisms.

The layman, explained Kincaid, is apt to forget that the bodies of the animals of the seashore, like men's, must be supplied with minerals, proteins, and carbohydrates. Nature provides the animals with this balanced diet as the tides sweep past them. After the water has given up its food materials to the animals, it is carried away by the retreating high tide to be replenished far out at sea.

Because an oyster sits on a piece of shell all its life, a number of special adjustments must be made to living. Douglas Welch, a Seattle newspaperman, wrote in one of his humorous articles: "When the oyster gets tired of being a male, he can become a female. He never knows when he gets up in the morning whether he ought to step into trousers or a silk print dress."

Kincaid, trying to improve on Welch's facetious remarks, quipped, "The oyster is able to change its personality and its habits as easily as did Dr. Jekyll and 'Mrs.' Hyde." This is particularly true of the native oyster, which is bisexual, one season a male and the next a female.

"Last spring," Kincaid rambled on, "the young native oysters were talking about politics and baseball. Now they are knitting tiny garments. Come winter and they will slip into a state of quietude in which they are neither Ned nor Nancy." The Pacific oyster, on the other hand, may be male or female several years running, but the males invariably turn into females about the third year and there is nothing they can do about it. (Of course, the process is not as simple and specific as these humorists lead us to believe, but their statements are fundamentally valid.)

Kincaid also discovered that on beaches with southern exposures, where the water is warmed as it comes in over long gentle sunny slopes, more and more oysters spawn naturally. The over-all summer temperatures, of course, continued to be the most important factor in their sexual responses. In his *Autobiography* he reported that in 1935 there was a good spawn, then for three years there was not a sign of spat. Between 1940 and 1942, "sets" were unusually good, which was fortunate because the combined spat of those years was enough to carry the industry through the war years when no importation of spat from Japan was possible.

A newspaperman, who had been sent to Nahcotta by a Seattle paper to check with Kincaid the report that clams were being poisoned by a "red tide," said "The Professor's mind is a veritable mine of ideas." After talking with him a short time, the reporter found himself growing more interested in the life force of the dedicated scientist, who was impelled to look ever deeper into the natural forces at work on the seashore, than he was in the clams.

To confirm or deny the question of the poisoned clams, Kincaid peered through his ever-present microscope. Almost immediately he identified the suspect as *Noctiluca,* a very common non-poisonous protozoan that lives in the surface waters during the warmer months, sometimes nearly covering the shores with a harmless bright red blanket (to be distinguished from the *Gonyaulax,* a poisonous red protozoan).

As proof of his confidence in the innocence of the *Noctiluca,* Kincaid without a moment's hesitation ate a dish of steamed clams from the suspected area. He topped off his meal by gulping down a number of barnacles. "They are rather good. Won't you have some?" he asked the reporter. "They taste much like shrimp."

Mrs. Kincaid, with a sly glance at her husband, added, "As you can see, our meals have often included sea urchins, sea cucumbers, and octopus, not to mention such delicacies as snails, frog legs, and seaweeds."

"And to my wife's eternal credit, she has willingly cooked them all. Through the years I have eaten all sorts of seashore life and I have come to a good old age with scarcely an ache or a pain. Of course, I'm not sure my diet is the reason for my good health. My Scotch-Irish ancestry may have had something to do with it. Who can say?" he joked.

The reporter put his notebook into his pocket and headed back to Seattle to report Kincaid's comments on the "red tide." In the last paragraph of his report he wrote, "Men such as Kincaid perform public services without pecuniary rewards and with but token appreciation for their services which rival or surpass those of many of the great inventors of the industrial world."

CHAPTER 11

Swiftly Fly
the Years

BUSY WITH HIS heavy teaching schedule, his work with the oysters, and his service to the public, Kincaid had yet another problem dropped into his lap in the summer of 1929. Great excitement was sweeping Seattle over what seemed to be an invasion of earwigs. Kincaid had seen earwigs in the area since 1907, but they had previously been considered merely a nuisance. Now the citizens feared that they would destroy the luxuriant flowers and shrubs of the Northwest.

The earwig, *Forticula auricularia*, it was known, lived in many parts of Europe, where there was a widespread belief that the insect entered a man's ear and from there bored into his brain. According to a bulletin put out by the United States Department of Agriculture, the origin of the superstition was a mystery, because there was no record of an earwig ever having entered the ear of any creature. However, the bulletin concluded, "It is possible the insect does so on rare occasions." It was, no doubt, this unfounded fear that was gripping Seattleites.

The earwig was an ugly black and brown creature, about an inch long, with short stiff antennae, strong chewing parts, and an abdomen that ended in a pair of prominent forceps. According to the bulletin it rarely flies, but travels widely at night. At the approach of day it crawls into bundles of newspapers, luggage, packages of merchandise, or any available container. It also scuttles in and out of bed linen, drops on the table from among cut flowers, and appears between pages of books. The bulletin also asserted that the earwig is as much at home in a garbage dump feeding upon dead fish as in the heart of a rose. Surely an unpleasant picture.

Discussion of the destructive pest had begun in 1927 in clubs and civic groups in Seattle. The City Council, the Health Department, and the County Horticultural Service each devoted $10,000 to establish a bureau to investigate the earwig problem. After a research study had been carried on for some months, the bureau decided to set up a baiting program to handle the problem.

A. S. Coyne, a "consulting entomologist," volunteered to do the baiting, and was placed at the head of the Bureau at a salary of $300 a month. Formerly Coyne had been an exterminator of rats and a fumigator of fruit on ships. At first, property owners were urged to bait on a voluntary basis. But in 1929, in spite of much opposition, Coyne insisted that the baiting be made compulsory. From the beginning, Kincaid and other biologists had favored the importation of a European beetle to control the pest.

To finance the compulsory baiting program the city and county contributed another $10,000 for work on parks, parking strips, and vacant lots. The cost of spreading the bait on an estimated 85,000 property owners' premises was to be paid by the owners at a rate of $1.25 per 40-foot lot, or at an overall cost of $125,000 annually. The program was to last at least two years.

From this point on, the earwig baiting program turned into a comic opera directed by the *Seattle Times*. The controversy over the unpopular campaign grew more and more bitter. Coyne insisted that the baiting be done by "professional baiters," who turned out to be University students. The baiters would apply for the jobs one day and then, armed with bags of earwig bait, go out the next day throwing a few handsful of bait across the lawns of citizens. (The formula for the bait was 5 pounds of bran, 2½ pounds of sugar, 2½ pounds of meat meal, and 10 ounces of paris green). This quantity was said to be sufficient to bait 4,000 square feet of lawn. An irate citizen in the Magnolia District complained, "I was visited by the baiting team and I thought I was entertaining Cox's army. The baiters apparently had never been in a garden before, for they tramped down shrubs, flowers, lawns in a three minute operation. The men were paid $5.00 for four hours of this desecration."

With a staff of seven regular secretaries and several assistants, Coyne launched a crash program with the employees working six-hour shifts from six o'clock in the morning until midnight, including Sundays. The Baiting Bureau, located in the Lyon Building, did a landslide business with orders barked out and countermanded in rapid succession as pandemonium reigned throughout the office. A battery of telephones rang constantly.

Thousands of citizens, aroused by what they called wanton waste, and convinced that the baiting was not reducing the number of earwigs, engaged in a controversy of such proportions that Acting Mayor Charles E. Carroll decided to call a halt to the nonsense and summoned a special meeting of city, county, and state officials concerned with control work. Trevor Kincaid was invited to attend the meeting as a guest, because many persons believed he was the only man in the area who could find a way to rid the city of the pest.

Coyne was asked to attend the meeting, but he flatly refused to answer questions. When called upon to speak, Kincaid calmly stated that nature can usually be depended upon to maintain a proper balance among the creatures of the earth. In fact, he assured the group, the earwig beetle, *Pterostichus vulgaris,* had already appeared in Seattle and was hard at work destroying the earwig. No one, he said, knew how the beetle had arrived here, but in all probability it had been brought in as a castaway with the importation of bulbs from Europe.

To prove the efficiency of the beetle, Kincaid explained that he had recently gathered a number of earwigs and beetles, put them in separate jars and displayed them in the window of Dresslar's Hardware store in the University District. Periodically he placed some of the beetles in the jar with the earwigs. In a few minutes the beetles had devoured the earwigs. As you can imagine, this graphic proof of the beetles' fondness for the earwig was pretty convincing. To the many viewers attracted to the show, the disappearance of the earwigs was almost like a magician's trick.

While Kincaid was speaking, he proved his point further by taking two glass jars from a small case saying, "I will give you a similar demonstration." He placed a dozen or more beetles in a jar, then put earwigs in the same jar and passed it to the man on his right, who in turn handed it to his neighbor. By the time the jar had gotten half way around the table, the earwigs were all reposing in the stomachs of the enemy. The officials needed no further proof of the efficiency of the beetle.

As a final argument, Kincaid said, "I haven't seen a single earwig suffer fatal effects from the poison. Expensive baits are never more than a temporary measure and no doubt do more harm than good by killing beneficial insects." Looking straight at Coyne, he continued, "During the month of June you scattered $125,000 worth of bait and along came a ten cent rain and washed it all away. You bait again for the next rain." A far sounder principle, he maintained, would be to marshal the earwig beetles and permit them to wage war in their own way. Coyne left the meeting without a word.

After weeks of consultations and interviews with committees and groups on the best methods of propagation and distribution of the earwig beetle, Kincaid returned to the study of oysters at Nahcotta. As he had predicted, the earwig beetle increased rapidly in numbers, and in a couple of months the threat of massive destruction by earwigs was checked. The professor felt certain the lowly earwig had been the innocent victim in the plot and that much of the damage to plant life in Seattle during recent years could be attributed largely to slugs.

Following the lead of the *Seattle Times,* thousands of disgruntled citizens demanded the dismissal of Coyne. But undaunted by the threat of curtailment of funds and his discharge, he and his "professionals" went blithely on with the work of baiting. He said it would take a third year and another $125,000 to completely rid the city of the pest. Kincaid retorted, "I suppose the earwigs in the unbaited half of the city will respect the red light at Denny Way and refuse to cross over into the clean side."

Citizens whose lots had been baited felt they should not have to pay the baiting bills. But the State Supreme Court ruled that according to state law, householders were responsible for the cost of the baiting. In February of the next year an article in the *Times* stated that 7,000 citizens were being taxed for the 1929 baiting and that unpaid charges would remain a lien against the property which might cloud the title.

It was not until November 15, 1932, that the *Times* wrote *finis* to the earwig farce by saying, "Well it begins to look as though the battle of the century between *Pterostichus vulgaris* and *Forticula auricularia* is nearing an end, with *Pterostichus* cleaning up on all points. It was pretty apparent from the first that when Trevor Kincaid stepped in as field marshal, the earwig hadn't a chance."

In any case, in the forty years since this comedy was staged in Seattle, earwigs have largely disappeared; the beetles are still preying upon them, upon cutworms, and upon other injurious insects; and little is heard about earwigs. Kincaid claimed that this is an example of the way in which nature effects a solution when allowed to carry out her own laws and illustrates the following verse:

> Great fleas have little fleas
> Upon their backs to bite 'em
> And little fleas have lesser fleas
> And so *ad infinitum.*

At the end of the summer when Kincaid returned to the University from his summer at Nahcotta Matthew Lyle Spencer had become President of the University, succeeding Henry Suzzallo. This change of administration brought frustrating problems to the University, especially to the faculty. Spencer evidently realized that his tenure of office would be determined by his relationship with Governor Hartley, for it was common gossip that the University was run by telephone from Olympia. Certainly there were sweeping changes in organization during Spencer's term of office, with frequent firings and hirings. Kincaid said, more in truth than in jest, "I found the best policy was to avoid attracting attention; otherwise my head might have gone under the administrative guillotine."

As an example of the manner in which University affairs were conducted, Kincaid described an incident that occurred when Dean Henry Landes of the College of Science requested him to serve as Dean while he was away on a leave of absence. A short time later, President Spencer called a deans' meeting. Various items of business were transacted and committees appointed. The meeting adjourned.

The next morning when Kincaid picked up the newspaper, he found that overnight Spencer had abolished the Board of Deans and had organized the University into four divisions, each with a super Dean, 'The Four Horsemen," they were called. Thus Kincaid punned, "My term as Dean was very short. Having been a dean and then duly canned, I was a sort of sardine."

In spite of political and professional unrest during Spencer's administration, the University, according to Kincaid, continued to grow; teaching was emphasized; faculty salaries were raised (then cut 32% during the Depression); and more buildings were

constructed during Spencer's term than during any
other period in the history of the University—Guggenheim Hall, Oceanographic Laboratory, Physics
Hall, Women's Physical Education Building, the
Men's Pavilion, Condon Hall. Thorough academic
training was emphasized, and the Graduate School
was greatly strengthened.

When the Orson Bennett Johnson Biology Building was erected in 1930 to replace the old Science
Hall built in 1902 (which was remodeled and renamed Parrington Hall), Dr. Hatch felt that Kincaid
was not enthusiastic about moving to the new building. His reluctance, Hatch believed, was due to his
long occupancy of the old building. He was at home
there. He knew where to find every record, every
insect box, every scrap of paper on which he had
scribbled notes for the past twenty-five years.

The veteran professor often joked about the disorder of his office, saying that visitors threw up their
hands, saying, "It looks like hell all stirred up with a
stick." This untidiness so bothered Belle Stevens, a
very methodical graduate student, that she undertook to bring order out of chaos. At the conclusion of
the operation, when everything was in its proper
drawer, shelf, or filing cabinet, all properly labeled,
Kincaid muttered, "Formerly only God and I knew
where to find everything. Now only God and Belle
Stevens know and I wouldn't be surprised if God isn't
sometimes puzzled." It took months for him to get
his office back to his special brand of "orderly confusion."

But whether in the old office or the new, the door
was always open. Even if every chair and table in the
room were piled with papers and books, the professor hurriedly brushed them aside and offered his visi-

tor a seat. His classes continued to attract large numbers of students with whom he maintained a relaxed, friendly relationship.

For example, as a final examination in the entomology course one spring, Kincaid asked the students to make a collection of fifty insects, properly labeled and mounted. A young man who realized the Professor's almost uncanny ability to recognize a species of insect decided to play a joke on him. On the day the collections were to be handed in, the boy walked into Kincaid's office, much puzzled about the classification of a beetle. "Professor, this critter has me guessing. It doesn't seem to fit anywhere. It must be a new species."

"Let's see if I can solve the mystery," said Kincaid. Immediately he saw that the wings of one beetle and the head of another had been glued to the body of a third. Very seriously he looked at the specimen through the microscope, turned it this way and that, and wrinkled his brow in puzzlement. Finally he said, "Indeed it is a new species, a very unusual one. Did it hum?"

"Oh, yes, sir, it did," the boy beamed.

Then Kincaid chuckled, "That definitely proves it. It's a hum bug."

"Shucks, I thought maybe I could fool you. But no luck."

"At least I'll give you credit for doing a good job of surgery," Kincaid said.

The interview ended with the professor and the "surgeon" joining in a hearty laugh.

With the termination of Hartley's eight years as Governor of Washington in 1933, Lyle Spencer submitted his resignation as President "in the interest of prompt reorganization."

During Hugo Winkenwerder's interim presidency (he was Dean of the School of Forestry), the Board of Regents began to look for a successor to Spencer. More than a year passed before the search committee announced in June 1934 that Dr. Lee Paul Sieg, an Iowan who had been trained as a physicist with a specialty in optical phenomena, had accepted the appointment. Dr. Sieg had held a three-cornered position as Dean of the Liberal Arts College, Dean of the College of Education, and Dean of the Graduate School at the University of Pittsburgh.

The people of Seattle and the state received news of the appointment with approval, even with enthusiasm. *Time* magazine, in commenting on Dr. Sieg's acceptance of the post, believed he was the right man for Washington, saying, "They [Washingtonians] saw a strapping six-footer of 54, with close cropped iron gray hair above a tough tanned face, who looked more like an army engineer than a college professor. They knew him to be one of their own kind—robust, unhurried, thoughtful, a son of pioneer stock who had stayed close to the soil." Kincaid, too, believed the appointment of Sieg was a good one.

Charles Gates summarized the administration of Sieg as neither showy nor dramatic, but without doubt during his twelve years as President (the longest presidential term in the University's history) the school made many solid advancements, particularly in amicable relations between the Regents, the faculty, and the state.

Sieg's appointment of a Tenure and Academic Freedom Committee assured the faculty of more democratic procedures in matters of hiring and firing. Trevor Kincaid, who through the years had seen faculty men of great promise leave the University because of a lack of security, felt this to be a most important step.

President Sieg realized, as President Kane had, that the University of Washington was in dire need of a sense of tradition and saw a strengthening of the role of the Alumni Association as a means to that end. To be great, Sieg said, a University must have the loyalty of the men and women who have served her, of her earlier students, and of those who have made her name famous throughout the nation and the world. He pointed out that, from a long-term point of view, a university is no stronger than the people who have been trained by her. As a step toward achieving cohesiveness within the Alumni Association, the President suggested that each year at the Commencement exercises, recognition be given to an alumnus who had made an outstanding contribution to the business or professional world.

At once the Alumni Association began to search for such a man. Naturally their thoughts turned toward Trevor Kincaid, who had been connected with the University since 1894 when he was a bottle-washer in the zoology department at a salary of $25 a month. Through the intervening years he had become one of the most honored members of the faculty. Within seven years he was promoted to a full professorship and head of the department. He had earned a Phi Beta Kappa key; was a charter member of Sigma Xi, national scientific honor society; was listed in *Who's Who in America* and in *American Men of Science;* belonged to dozens of national professional societies; and was active in local groups—the Puget Sound Academy of Science, Phi Sigma, the Northwest Bird and Mammal Society. In 1931 he had been elected to membership in the Research Society. He had acquired a world-wide reputation as an entomologist; he had served as a United States emissary for scientific studies to a number of foreign countries; he had developed the valuable oyster industry; he had founded the Biological Station at Friday Harbor; and he had made innumerable contributions to the citizens of the state of Washington.

With all these achievements, it was not surprising that he alone was suggested as the first recipient of *Alumnus Summa Laude Dignitatus,* and thereby was acknowledged to be one of the most famous men the University of Washington had produced.

The bestowal of this honor was the highest tribute the University and the Alumni Association could give to one of her sons. In saluting Kincaid, the Association saluted itself, for he had been a part of the University before any of the present physical plant was built or any member of the present faculty was connected with the school. Through fifty years he had remained a symbol of the dedication and loyalty of the pioneer teachers, yet he had always kept abreast of scientific advances. One of Kincaid's colleagues, in congratulating him on this signal honor, said, "You always were a lucky fellow." Kincaid answered, "Well, maybe I have been lucky, but I have always noticed that the harder one works, the luckier he becomes."

Another recognition came to Kincaid in 1938 when an Honorary Doctor of Science degree was conferred upon him by the College of Puget Sound. Again some of his friends said, perhaps with a touch of envy, "Instead of accumulating wealth as some men do, Kincaid has collected honors." These kudos came as complete surprises to him, and gratified beyond expression, he accepted them with humility and pleasure.

Trevor Kincaid became seventy in 1942, and according to University regulations, it was time for him to retire. The chairmanship of the zoology department was offered to Dr. Arthur Svihla, a very competent administrator, who had been in the department for several years.

It was hard to think of the zoology department without Kincaid. During the half century he had been with the University, through good times and bad, his loyalty had never swerved. Through most of those years financial support of the university had been less than adequate. Realizing the shortage of money, Kincaid had been most frugal in the operation of the Department of Zoology. Even as late as his retirement his annual budget was a mere $6,000. In all probability he never asked for a raise in salary for himself, remaining one of the lowest paid heads of a department on the campus.

In spite of his own very limited resources, he had quietly aided scores of students by financing their work at Friday Harbor and helping them meet financial crises. He often interceded with the administration for leniency in dealing with promising foreign students who were faced with overwhelming problems in a new country. And in almost every case in which he saw a student through a difficult period, his judgment of character and ability proved to be correct. He also inspired many a young man by taking him on a field trip or to a scientific meeting. But possibly the major reasons for Kincaid's appeal to students were that he was first and last a human being and that he never set down moral judgments.

In return, the fifty thousand or more students who passed through his classes came to love the carelessly dressed man with the bug net and the hearty laugh as a gentleman, a scholar, and a friend. It is doubtful too that any student ever forgot the force of his personality, his cryptic comments, or his puns. The story is told of a colleague who was always suggesting to Kincaid that he "cooperate" with every passing project. Kincaid, having become weary of his expansive friend's arguments, answered, "That's fine. You 'co' and I'll 'operate,' as I have always done."

Kincaid may not have been an especially efficient administrator, for under him the department, which for many years was a one-man operation, had grown so gradually, and he was so familiar with every detail of the procedures, that he did not realize that new faculty members needed guidance and supervision. Without a firm and generally understood departmental policy, inexperienced men were apt to follow their own interests instead of the specific needs of the department.

Through the years a few men were appointed in the zoology department who did not work wholeheartedly with their executive officer. Too, in recent years the study of zoology had broadened to include many new fields. Kincaid had remained a morphologist and an entomologist, and he was not always in complete sympathy with newer, more specialized phases of zoological study. (At the time of Kincaid's retirement there were twelve full-time staff members and a score or more of teaching assistants.)

Also, he was among the last of the so-called naturalists, men who were concerned with the study of many aspects of natural history, which accounts, no doubt, for his calling himself an "omnologist." During Kincaid's youth and early manhood, highly technical apparatus had been difficult to obtain and very costly, so biologists of his generation of necessity studied the more obvious, more easily recognized characteristics of an animal or plant.

On a June Saturday in 1943, Trevor Kincaid marched in the academic procession of the University of Washington for the last time. At the conclusion of the exercises a newspaper reporter asked the retired professor about his most precious memories of half a century as a faculty member.

Thoughtfully Kincaid answered, "Although I have gone on scientific missions to many countries, received dozens of honors, had more than half a hundred plants and animals named after me, and have written many papers, contacts with students have always given me the most satisfaction. Like all of us who are teachers at heart, my greatest pleasure is recalling the opportunities I have given students to make something of themselves. I have watched their careers with interest and satisfaction." Then he added jokingly, "We have a brain factory out here. I guess we can call it that. I've helped polish up a few minds, put gas in their tanks, and oiled them up ready to go. Above all I have tried to make students conscious of the beautiful world about us. No student can go far wrong who really sees and understands the work of the 'one great spirit as revealed through nature.' "

After having a battery of cameras turned upon him, he took off his academic regalia (by this time green and frayed), and sat down at his desk in the book-cluttered office. He was leaving all this. He looked at the books, the mementos, the newspaper clippings, the kodak pictures, and shook his head. How had the years flown by so quickly?

And what should he do with the accumulation of a lifetime? A thousand events inextricably tied up with these memorabilia flashed through his mind; it would be hard to part with them. But scientific man that he was, he knew they must go. So he began to sort, to throw away, to give gifts—anything his colleagues, former students, and friends would like. His published papers, of course, were on file in the University Library. The disposition of the records and the miscellaneous notes did not bother him. The library was eager to have them, for among the boxes of random jottings was not only information about Kincaid, but also material that was extremely valuable historically.

Early records of the University of Washington, like those of many institutions, often had been lost or were merely reminiscences, which were almost sure to be full of inaccuracies. Kincaid's comments would do much to verify or refute statements about the early days. Finally, he moved the essential and best-loved possessions to a small room just off his former office. Other material he took to his home, "where, fortunately I have a large lower floor where I can spread out."

A few days after Kincaid bade farewell to the campus, his colleagues and former students honored him with a banquet replete with speeches, jokes, and personal tributes. A former graduate student, Luther Claire Altman, was toastmaster. In his response to the many tributes paid him, Kincaid emphasized his lifelong conviction that chance favors only the mind that is prepared and that nothing of real worth is achieved except through great effort. "You graduate students," he said, "who are just entering the ranks of professional scholars would have not achieved your goals without intense concentration and hard work."

Gordon Alcorn, who had recently earned a doctor's degree under Kincaid, responded by saying, "Of course, we worked hard, but no matter how difficult our problems they always were made easier by you quietly saying, 'I'm sure we can work it out.' That sentence is, no doubt, your most famous expression. I doubt if you could have lived the long, successful life you have had without it." Kincaid used it not only in dealing with students, but also with his associates in general. All his life he avoided disputes, saying that if a matter is approached calmly and with a touch of humor and a little "give and take" on both sides, it can almost always be worked out.

When the speeches had been delivered, Kincaid displayed the gift of a radio and a "diploma" designed especially for the occasion. Around the edges of the certificate were illustrations of some of the seventy plants and animals given the name "kincaidii." In the center was a quotation from Mark Akenside's eighteenth-century poem "Invectus":

> He many creatures did collectivize
> Almost unpeopling water, air and land.
> Fish, oysters, worms, snails, caterpillars, flies
> Were laid full low by his unrelenting hand.
> Could tell if a mite were lean or fat
> And read a lecture o'er the entrails of a gnat.

In honor of Kincaid's long career, Dr. Hatch wrote a history of the zoology department and a series of three papers: *Studies Honoring Trevor Kincaid,* published by the University of Washington Press. One was a sketch of Kincaid's life; another was based on the career of Orson Bennett Johnson; and the third was an account of the Young Naturalists' Society. Eight of the fifteen students who had earned Doctor of Philosophy degrees under Kincaid's tutelage also contributed to the study. (Although attempts had been made to establish a graduate school as early as 1889, it was not until the late 1920's that a significant Ph.D. program was set up on a firm basis.)

Despite the large number of Kincaid's published papers, it has been said that they did not represent his full potentialities. He had always been a man of action with a restless mind, more concerned with inquiring than in recording. In the early years Kincaid and other biologists of the area were over-whelmed by the wealth of materials to be studied, and it was hard to say what was of paramount impor-tance—collecting or publishing.

In 1943 when Kincaid retired, the United States was in the middle of World War II. The enrollment of the University dropped by 3,500 students. When a hundred faculty members went into military ser-vice, competent teachers were desperately needed, and Kincaid was called back to the school he loved to teach his favorite courses, limnology and plankton.

After four years as a part-time teacher, he retired a second time. His hair was somewhat whiter, and his step a little slower, but his eyes were as keen, and his energy and good humor as vibrant as ever. He knew, however, that the old must make place for the young, so he picked up his books, his insect net, and his unfinished research and walked off the campus. Tre-vor Kincaid's active participation in the affairs of the University was over, if the teaching of classes is all a lifetime of devotion to a school meant. But who can estimate the influence of such a man upon the thousands of students whose lives he touched?

As soon as Kincaid's retirement was announced, the telephone started ringing; the public was back plying him with questions. An airline stewardess who had just arrived from Alaska called him on the telephone in great excitement; "Oh, Professor Kincaid, I have a mastodon's tooth. May I bring it out right away?" Taking a taxi from the airport, she arrived at Kincaid's home in record time, carrying the great fang in her arms. She asked breathlessly, "How old is it?"

The professor examined it carefully, turned it this way and that, then answered with an impish grin, "Perhaps half a million years. Oh, of course, I may be off a year or two either way." Later he said, "I couldn't see what all the hurry was about since the tusk had already been lying around for thousands of years." A man from Uruguay asked for information about diatoms. A student from California wanted a certain species of crustacean, and so it went.

One constantly recurring question was, "What is the difference between students today and when you started teaching?"

He always answered, "They have changed in many ways, but two things have remained constant—freshmen and human nature. I have especially enjoyed watching the sons and daughters of former students, sometimes even the grandchildren and discovering the same personalities and mannerisms and even the same deviltry appearing in later generations of a family."

A most annoying question came from a man who asked, "What is the study of insects all about? A man chasing insects with a net seems so foolish and how can you make any money doing it?" For the hundredth time the professor patiently explained that all scientific work directly or indirectly benefits mankind. Occasionally there is a dramatic example of the value of the bug net and the flyswatter, such as the discovery that mosquitoes carried the germs of malaria and yellow fever. This knowledge, as everyone knows today, wiped out the dread scourge of these diseases at the time of the building of the Panama Canal and brought health to many tropical lands.

Then, of course, he continued, there was the work Sir Alexander Fleming was doing with molds, apparently just for idle curiosity, but a curiosity which resulted in the discovery of penicillin, the wonder drug that has saved countless lives.

"What is the value of pure research when there are so many important practical problems to be solved?", asked a strong-minded woman. The value of pure research was a subject very near to Kincaid's heart. "Americans," he would say, with surprising heat for him, "are just beginning to realize the close relationship between pure science and applied science. Pure science is sometimes called a waste of time, just busy work, yet, no doubt, half the great scientific discoveries in the world have been the outcome of someone merely wanting to know, wondering 'why.' "

For example, Einstein's abstract mathematical deductions were an early step in nuclear research. Leonardo da Vinci's study of the flight of birds in the sixteenth century was perhaps the first suggestion of airplanes. And a casual watching of the wings of bats gave the initial clue to radar waves. Today researchers are trying to ferret out the properties of the magically strong adhesive produced by barnacles in the hope of duplicating it to secure fillings in human teeth. Certainly curiosity is the basis of all learning, and a student with a lot of plain inquisitiveness often far outdistances his more placid fellows.

Although Kincaid could no longer serve the University, the Shell Fish Laboratory, a division of the State Department of Fisheries, desperately needed a man of his talents. The men at the head of this group knew his experience and knowledge of oyster culture were too valuable to go unused. So when he was asked to continue his work with them, he accepted the assignment with the enthusiasm of a boy.

He loaded his car with reference books, preserving fluids, and microscopes, and he and Louise set out for their tiny cabin in Nahcotta, which offered them peace, quiet, far horizons, and the pungent salty odors of the sea. And thus he began an eleven-year project as an adviser to the State Fisheries Department.

The seashore was such an ingrained part of Kincaid's inner self that with the first whiff of salt air his spirit was uplifted. He gained a new awareness of its beauty and deeper meaning, thereby renewing in him the urge to wrestle with a new idea, to make a fresh observation, or to write another paper, to know more.

A quotation from Rachel Carson's book, *Under the Sea Wind,* expresses Kincaid's philosophy exactly:

To stand at the edge of the sea, to sense the ebb and flow of the tides, to feel the breath of the mist over a great salt marsh, to watch the flight of the shore birds that have swept up and down the surf of the continents for thousands of years, to see the running of old eels and the young shad to the seas—is to have a knowledge of things that are as nearly eternal as any life can be.

During his long years of service at the Shell Fish Laboratory, Kincaid worked as hard as he had in his youth, and his unflagging zeal did much to bring the industry to a high degree of success. Shortly before leaving the Laboratory in 1951, he gave an address to the Oyster Growers Association, in which he said, "If I am the father of the oyster industry in Washington, as you say, I would like to present this industrial baby for your inspection and blessing."

He explained that in 1922 when the first 400 cases of oysters were shipped to Washington from Japan, it was an infant industry whose success no one could predict. By 1931 it had graduated to rompers with the Willapoint and other companies supplying thousands of gallons of fresh refrigerated oysters for the local markets. By 1936, to push the analogy further, it was a husky youth, with oysters and oyster products being converted by many companies into marketable forms at the rate of a million dollars a year. That year the steam pack sent 118,533 cans of oysters to the distributing centers of the nation. Today, he said, $6,000,000 worth of processed oysters were harvested on the Pacific Coast and products from Willapa Bay produced $4,000,000 of that amount. The most recent additions to the market were soup and smoked oysters, which are going to all parts of the world. "This growth," Kincaid continued, "seems to me to represent quite an achievement when business was supposed to be sulking in her tent" (meaning the Depression).

In conclusion, he warned the growers that today oyster culture in Washington is at the crossroads. Will it continue to develop along lines it has followed for the past thirty-five years? Will industrial development on the shores introduce wastes and other conditions injurious to its operation, or will artificial methods of cultivation be used? Already, in many parts of the globe, oysters are being produced artificially. Using new methods, oyster scientists far from salt water beaches can now make oysters available at all seasons of the year.

Trevor Kincaid was now 84 years of age. He realized he could no longer hustle over the oyster beds as nimbly as he once had, and it was time to turn the work over to younger scientists. So at the end of August he made one final inspection of a particularly productive bed, removed his beach boots, covered his microscopes, picked up his books, locked the door of his cabin, and bade farewell to Willapa Harbor.

But when the Kincaids reached home there was no hub-bub of children's voices, no patter of little feet, no tales of "while you were away," as in former years. The children were all married and gone to homes of their own. Looking around the house, which seemed too large, Trevor remarked, "The house is certainly quiet, isn't it? Maybe we should get a parrot to chatter to us." Then they recalled the children's small triumphs and disappointments as they progressed through University Heights Elementary School, John Marshall Junior High, Roosevelt High School, and the University of Washington. Louise turned to the telephone saying, "I must tell Polly we are home. I'm sure she will come right over."

Trevor looked at his wife and smiled, "We have a goodly heritage."

CHAPTER 12

Is This Retirement?

EVEN AT 85, Kincaid was not ready to sit with folded hands before the fireplace. He still believed that teaching and involvement in work were the most rewarding things in life and kept him young at heart. There were many projects to keep him busy.

For the first couple of weeks after returning home from Willapa Bay, he wandered around the yard trying to help Louise with the garden, but she said he was useless as a gardener because he was more concerned with the insects on the plants than he was in pulling weeds. One morning he spied some beetles on the roots of the wisteria vine that covered the trellis above the dining room windows. He got down on his knees to see them more closely.

Aram Langhaus, a ten-year-old boy who lived across the street, hurried over to Kincaid and asked in a charming Viennese accent, "Have you lost something, Professor?"

"No, I am finding something. You know, a very populous, unseen and almost unknown world of minute creatures live in a garden of this size. I thought I might discover a species of insect I had never found before. Anyone can see an elephant or a dog, but it takes a trained eye and a concern for all life to seek out the insignificant creatures."

"Let me help you," said Aram. Soon the elderly man with close-cropped gray hair and the boy, alert and quick with shiny black locks, were busy gathering tiny forms of life and looking at them through Kincaid's magnifying glass. Kincaid knew at once he had discovered a disciple, a boy with a curious mind. One of his problems of retirement was solved then and there—an eager student.

Later that afternoon Aram and Wendy, his young sister, came knocking at Kincaid's door. "Oh, Professor, look what we found. Our rose bushes are covered with little green bugs. What are they?" Carefully Aram removed the cover from a bottle. Out crawled a dozen or more aphids.

"They are aphids, very destructive little creatures. If you don't get rid of them right away they will destroy all your roses. I'll give you some rose spray. But first let's look at the culprits through the microscope in my downstairs laboratory."

In a few days word of the wonders of Kincaid's microscope had spread through the neighborhood and his disciples quickly grew in numbers. Early the next Monday morning Matt Riley appeared at Kincaid's door carrying a large box. "Oh, Professor, I found a humdinger of a specimen. I want you to tell me what it is."

"Let's see the humdinger. I've never met an insect by that name and I'm glad to make its acquaintance," laughed Kincaid. From the box Matt carefully lifted a large fly with a wing spread of four inches or more, the delicate pattern of its wings almost like gossamer. "It's a honey, isn't it?"

"Yes, it is. It's a lace fly, a rare species, I think. Where did you find it?"

The Kincaid home at 1904 North East 52nd Street, Seattle.

Louise and Trevor Kincaid celebrating their fortieth wedding anniversary on August 23, 1957, with their children (left to right), Marjorie, Dorothy, Barbara, Thomas Farrar, Polly, and Kathleen.

"At our summer place on Stillaguamish River. Dad says you can tell me what it is, for you know everything about bugs and plants and oysters."

"I have a book that describes the range of the lace fly. If this species isn't reported from Washington we will send it to the National Museum for identification," said Kincaid leading the way toward his library.

"Wouldn't it be something if it is rare? I might become famous like you," concluded Matt.

Soon another group of boys were at the door. "Professor, come out quick," they urged. "There are some strange birds in the hawthorne trees. The robins are trying to drive them away."

Kincaid pattered in short, quick steps across the garden at the heels of the young callers. Perched on a low branch of the hawthorne tree was a flock of evening grosbeaks with large yellow bills and striking feathered coats of black, yellow, and white.

"They're evening grosbeaks, early spring visitors in Seattle," explained Kincaid. "They're probably on their way north to nest. They will be gone in a week or two when they are fed and rested and have stripped the trees of berries." Off the boys went on another trail of discovery.

But Aram and Wendy remained the most devoted students of entomology. "I'm so glad you showed us how to use a microscope," volunteered Wendy. "Even the tiniest bug looks big and beautiful when magnified. The shiny, hard covering on the back of the June bug is like a suit of armor."

"Guess we never used our eyes before we met you. But we're learning. I see lots of things now I didn't know existed before we began collecting insects," added Aram. "Dad said he will buy me a microscope for Christmas if I get good grades in school."

"Those children have quick minds and are eager to investigate everything," Trevor remarked to Louise as she prepared his usual bowl of oyster soup for lunch. "I love to teach them. It's almost like being back in the classroom."

Kincaid's second goal in retirement was to complete some of the research work he had begun years before. He wrote a paper describing the development of the oyster industry, which was printed by a local company, but there were many delays and disappointments and the cost was more than he had anticipated.

Remembering the neighborhood news sheet he and his brother had printed when they were boys, he decided to produce his own writings. After a long search he located a second-hand Kelsey press with a printing area 8 X 10 inches. He bought several fonts of type and soon was in business as publisher, editor, typesetter, pressman, and printer's devil.

He called his publishing venture the Calliostoma Press. "For all I know *Calliostoma* may be the name of some long forgotten mythological god, but I chose it because it is the name of a genus of beautiful snail found on Puget Sound beaches."

When Kincaid talked of the papers he would print, he shook his head, wrinkled his brow, and chuckled, "The books from my press will have a very limited edition and still smaller audience. You won't find them on the best seller list. Probably not more than fifteen persons in the world care about the obscure creatures I write about, but I will send them to my scientific friends in all parts of the world. A few people may even buy them."

The first production of the Calliostoma Press was his *Autobiography,* of which he made but two copies. "I want my grandchildren to know what sort of a fellow I was." The next paper was a "Contribution to the Taxonomy and Distribution of a Fresh Water Calonoid Crustacean." From his bulging files and from his prodigious memory, he printed seventy-five pages of text and made five plates of pictures describing this previously unrecorded species. When the printing was completed, he developed and reproduced the illustrations, bound the volumes by sewing the pages together by hand, enclosed the study in heavy, blue paper covers, put them in envelopes, and sent a hundred or more reprints to zoologists from Russia to Afghanistan.

When he was invited to discuss West Coast oyster culture at a meeting of fisheries scientists in Miami, the Kincaids bought a new Chrysler and set out on a three-month journey from the Pacific to the Atlantic oceans. When their plans were announced, they received so many invitations they could not possibly accept them all.

In the home of Harriet and Don Frizzell in Rolla, Missouri, the conversation was about the summers they had spent at Friday Harbor—dredging trips, tunicates, barnacles, the *Medea*, and, and, and "It would take a week to recall all the interesting things we did there," Harriet concluded.

Finally Kincaid interrupted, "But did you learn any marine biology? I've heard only about the frosting on the cake."

"Did we? We learned more about the wonders of the sea in those nine weeks than in a whole year of conventional classes. Somehow the sea and the universe became alive and meaningful to us."

In New England the Kincaids visited Louise's Yankee relatives, whom she had not seen for twenty years. And again there was much talk, not about tunicates and barnacles, but about the first Farrar who came from England in 1747 and who was killed by Indians and about great-grandfather Timothy Farrar, who was a law partner of Daniel Webster in New Hampshire.

Even with the pre-Revolutionary Farrar family, Louise and Trevor Kincaid could not linger, for they had traveled three thousand miles to see oyster beds and oyster canning plants.

When Kincaid was introduced at the meeting in Miami, a cheer went up from the audience. At the close of his remarks, the chairman stopped the applause and asked how many in the hall had worked with Kincaid. Hands went up all over the room. Kincaid was almost overcome by the appreciation and acclaim accorded him.

After leaving Miami, the Kincaids enjoyed the beautiful white sand beaches of Florida and Mississippi, where in spite of his wife's instructions not to get his fingernails black or his new suit dirty by grubbing in the sand, Trevor could not resist the temptation to pop a few unusual shells into his pocket. Their odyssey terminated in Santa Barbara with a longer visit and a rest with Louise's sister and her doctor husband.

Back in Seattle after his tour around the United States, Kincaid began once more to search through his unfinished manuscripts. He had been greatly stimulated by contacts with zoologists across the country, and he felt he must get back to work. The project he decided to complete was material that had been stored in his mind since the turn of the century.

One afternoon in those long-gone days during a casual collecting trip along a primitive waterway that connected Lake Washington and Lake Union (the present Lake Washington canal was not begun until 1911), he had passed his net over a clump of reddish plants, *Orthocarpus pusillus,* and found on their stems a number of black ants, which to his surprise were fertilizing the flowers. Some distance farther, he again found the ants on the stems of the plant.

Of course, he knew that many plants are fertilized by insects, but the relationship between plants and ants had apparently never been noted by entomologists. As was his wont, Kincaid stored this information in his mind for further verification. Years later during his summers at Willapa Bay he again saw ants fertilizing *Orthocarpus pusillus* or ant plant.

After returning from Florida, he reread the original notes and looked at the pictures of the ant plant he had taken so long ago. He then checked the literature and found that this animal and plant relationship was still unrecorded. Unlike rapidly changing conditions in the political or social world of man, changes in the world of nature are slow and time is endless, so the passage of years between his first observation of this phenomenon and his recording of it did not alter its validity. After working on the project for weeks, he felt he had sufficient proof to state his findings with some degree of certainty. Again Kincaid began turning the crank of his old-fashioned press and another research paper was ready for distribution.

His longest and most ambitious paper was "Local Races and Clines of the Marine Snail *Thais lamellosa,*" an abundant species commonly called the purple snail because the Romans are said to have used it in dyeing their royal purple togas. For many years he had gathered these snails, noticing that the shells from each promontory, island, or isolated reef varied

slightly in form and markings from those in every
other locality. He had thousands of shells from hundreds of areas. The paper attracted considerable attention not only among zoologists but also among
paleontologists because it showed how local conditions affect the unbelievably slow changes involved
in evolution. The paper consisted of twenty pages of
text and fifty pages of illustrations showing the variations in texture and markings of the shells.

In 1958, under a joint authorship with Kincaid, Dr.
Hatch catalogued 500 species of beetles which Kin-
caid and he had collected over a number of years.
The paper was titled "List of Coleoptera, from the
Vicinity of Willapa Harbor." In 1965 the journal of
the American Microscopical Society, an influential
scientific organization, published "A Problematic
Sense Organ Found upon Stahyinid Beetles."

Several of Kincaid's recent papers, Dr. Hatch said,
ranked high among the research he had done and are
a lasting record of his wide knowledge of seashore
life. They also prove that a man's contribution to
science and to knowledge need not terminate with
his retirement.

In 1957 it did not seem possible to Louise and
Trevor Kincaid that they had been married forty
years. They had been years of happiness, of hard
work, of good health, of good family relationships,
and of considerable financial strain, all of which had
welded their lives and hearts into an indissoluble
union. To celebrate this important event, the Kincaids, surrounded by their six children, their sons-in-
law, their daughter-in-law, and their twenty-one
grandchildren, greeted dozens of friends in the parlor of the Plymouth Congregational Church where
they had been married. Swelling with pride, the

grandfather snapped pictures of the family, "a very fine, handsome group" he boasted and he might have added, "and successful too."

The first break in the family circle came in the summer of 1964 with the death of Louise Kincaid from cancer. To the last day of her life, this gallant lady loved and admired "her professor." Through the years her love had been selfless, her object always to protect his time and his peace of mind. In spite of his forgetful ways, his wrinkled clothes, his absorption with scientific projects, his erratic working hours, to Louise "he was just right as he was." He was her world.

In his turn, especially during her last illness, he was her humble lover—bringing her flowers, carrying the evening paper to her bedside, recounting the amusing incidents of the day, straightening the bed covers, giving her a kiss and saying "good night, my dear. I love you. You have made me very happy."

Without his ever devoted helpmate, Trevor felt lost, but he continued to live in his home in the University District. "It's all the permanence I have left," he said. His daughters Dorothy, Polly, and Kathleen came regularly to clean the house and to cut their father's still wayward hair. (The other two daughters lived far from Seattle.) His son's children spent the week with their grandfather while attending the University but returned to their home in Edmonds for weekends.

Kincaid gradually adjusted himself to being alone, for he had never been dependent upon people. He had never concerned himself with University politics; he had never played handball with his colleagues; he had never gone to bridge or cocktail parties; he had never donned a dinner jacket for a

Trevor Kincaid helping his "disciple" Wendy Langhans identify an insect (May 17, 1964).

visiting dignitary. Once, however, at an afternoon
garden reception at the Lake Washington beach
home of President Spencer he had worn an old-fashioned morning suit and a pair of white gloves. After
greeting the President, the Deans, and a few old
friends, Kincaid slowly made his way to the pier at
the end of the garden. Soon he was kneeling on the
dock, his coattails flying, trying to extract a small
wriggling fish from the water. By this time the eyes
of half the guests were on the dauntless collector.
Louise calmly walked to the dock saying, "Trevor,
it's time to go home." He had always maintained he
would rather watch a spider spin its web (or catch a
fish) than shake hands with the President.

Now that he was alone, he worked from eight
o'clock in the morning until ten at night, searching
through manuscripts or consulting notes for his writings. Then he went to bed (a daybed in the living
room) and read a mystery novel until the wee hours
of the morning. His scientific notes, his typewriter,
his microscope were always within easy reach. The
card table at which he worked stood beside his chair.
Books were stacked on chairs, on tables, on the floor,
as of yore. Dr. Hatch remained an important link
between him and the Department of Zoology.

The public still plied Kincaid with questions, per-
taining both to life today and to conditions long past
and gone, expecting him to be both prophet and
historian. He frequently had out-of-town visitors,
many of them elderly men he had known long ago.
Their conversations consisted mostly of reminiscences, their laughter booming out at the memory of
a prank or an especially humorous event.

When the class of 1916 held its fiftieth reunion,
they invited Kincaid, who had been their class spon-

sor, to join the festivities. When the committee who were to extend the invitation arrived at his home, they found him stirring the embers in the fireplace with a poker. "What are you doing?" a visitor asked.

"I'm gold mining," he chuckled. "My grandson gave me a piece of caramel candy and like a fool I started to chew it. I was talking and the caramel pulled a gold filling out of my teeth and it fell into the fire. Now I am sleuthing for it." (He never found the filling).

The declining years of Kincaid's life moved along serenely. He did not go out often, but the family gathered at their father's home for his birthday and for Christmas, cooperating in supplying a festive meal. They dropped in often to see him. With the passing of the years, remarkably good communication had developed between them.

Of course, Kincaid's body showed the passage of time. When callers came, he adjusted his hearing aid, saying "How I hate this miserable thing." Yet his general health was so good that after each regular checkup, the doctor said, "You're as sound as a winter apple."

On December 22, 1967, Trevor Kincaid turned 95. He now had a nurse-housekeeper to look after his needs. However, his mind was almost as keen as it had ever been. He admitted he had forgotten the names of many of his former students. "I only recall those who were particularly brilliant or those who were too lazy to study. But if put to it, I'm sure I could recall thousands of insignificant animals by their long Latin scientific names."

In the spring of that year the indefatigable man embarked upon a most interesting research project —an ecological survey of Willapa Bay. For forty years

he had watched the development of the oyster industry there very closely. Recently he had noticed that
the Pacific oysters, which at first had often grown to
be ten or more inches long, had become much
smaller. (The public thought the smaller ones more
appetizing.) "What could account for this reduction
in size?" he asked himself. As he had done so many
times, he now said, "Why? Let's find out."

Was it the biological conditions in the bay; shortage of plankton on which the oysters fed; geological
changes in the tideflats; the tremendous amount of
fresh water poured into the ocean by the Columbia
River; the chemistry of the water; the weather? He
knew that to make a thorough investigation of all the
factors was an extremely long, complicated problem,
one that would call into play his knowledge of many
branches of science, his being an "omnologist."

In speaking of plans for the work, he said, "Since
I cannot visit the Bay myself, I am dependent upon
the literature and samples brought to me. It is ques-
tionable that I will live long enough to make a comprehensive study of all the phases of the study, but at
least I will have opened it up for other scientists to
carry on." After months of investigations his tentative conclusion was that so much oyster spat had
been planted on the beds that there was no longer
enough calcium in the water to make the large shells.
Of course, calcium is continually being replaced by
the incoming tides, but it would seem that in this case
the natural balance that exists in nature had been
disturbed by overplanting.

Other chemicals such as manganese, which may
play a role in the biosynthesis of amino acids and in
reproduction may also have become unbalanced. But
Kincaid realized these imbalances may be only minor factors in the overall answers. His conclusions did

not indicate that the bay is less productive than formerly, but they did suggest that men have over-exploited the oyster beds.

The conclusions drawn from this study were published under the title, "The Ecology of Willapa Bay."

Without question, the highest of Kincaid's accolades came to him on the eve of his ninety-seventh birthday, when Dr. Charles Odegaard, President of the University of Washington, went to his home to announce that the Board of Regents had voted to name a new building on the campus Trevor Kincaid Hall. At the same time the President gave him a framed sketch of the proposed building. This action of the Regents, Dr. Odegaard said, was a departure from the long-established practice of naming buildings only in recognition of faculty members, friends, or benefactors of the school who had died.

The present action was a tribute to Kincaid's seventy-five years of service as a teacher; loyal friend of the state of Washington; world-wide ambassador of the United States in seeking solutions to biological problems; continuing interest in research during twenty years of retirement; and certainly to the dignity and grace he had maintained at arriving at this extreme old age.

In acknowledging his pride and gratitude to the President for the honor, Kincaid laughed in his characteristic hearty manner, and said, "Well, I guess I have come full circle. In 1892 when I was twenty a tiny microscopic parasite was given the name *kincaidii.* Now at 97 a University building will bear my name. I can't go much further than that academically."

Trevor Kincaid passed away on July 2, 1970, on the one hand the artist of the good life, and on the other the natural scientist, who had spent his life in the

Kincaid Hall, dedicated in May, 1972, on the University of Washington campus.

service of science and his fellow men. All he ever asked in return for his countless services to the University of Washington and the students was the freedom to worship God in the beautiful world about him, to work, to be himself, to open new windows, to follow his own goals, and to answer that ever baffling "why?".

In childhood in Canada, in Olympia, in Alaska, in Japan, in Russia, in a one-room cottage, in a tent at Friday Harbor, in an emperor's palace, on a millionaire's boat, or in his cluttered office in Science Hall, in his home in Seattle, Trevor Kincaid had enjoyed every stage of his life. He had lived to the utmost, meeting every challenge with an unswerving faith in the essential goodness of God and man—in Life itself.

And as the end of his life drew near he could say with Emerson:

> As the bird trims her to the gale,
> I trim myself to the storms of time
> I man the rudder, reef the sail
> Obey the voice at eve, obeyed at prime.

Plants and Animals Named in Honor of Trevor Kincaid

Mastigophora

Peridinium kincaidi Wailes, Protozoa and Algae from Mount Hopeless, B.C. Art, Hist. and Sci. Assoc., Vancouver, B.C., Nov. 1, 1933, p. 3, fig. 8–12 (mimeographed).

Foraminifera

Polymorphina kincaidi Cushman and Todd, Cushman Lab. for Foraminiferal Research Special Pub. 21, 1947, p. 12.

Coelenterata

Campanularia kincaidi Nutting, Proc. U.S. Nat. Mus. 21, 1899, p. 743.

Diphasia kincaidi (Nutting), Am. Nat. 35, 1901, p. 789; described in Thuiaria.

Oligochaeta

Enchytraeus kincaidi Eisen, Harriman Alaska Exp. 12, 1904, p. 66.

Kincaidiana n. gen. Altman, Univ. Wash. Publ. Biol. 4 (1), 1936, p. 64.

Mesenchytraeus kincaidi Eisen, Harriman Alaska Exp. 12, 1904, p. 40.

Plutellus kincaidi Altman, Univ. Wash. Publ. Biol. 4 (1), 1936, p. 74.

Pelecypoda

Pecten (Chlamys) hindsii kincaidi Oldroyd, Nautilus, 33, 1920, pp. 135–136.

Tellina kincaidi Weaver, Wash. Geol. Surv. Bull. no. 15, 1912, pp. 64–65.

Gastropoda

Clione kincaidi Agersborg, Ann. Sci. Nat. Zool. (10) 6, 1923, p. 392.

Coralliophora (Pseudomurex) kincaidi Dall, Proc. U.S. Nat. Mus. 56, 1919, pp. 339–340.

Kincaidella Hannibal, Pr. Mal. Soc. London 12, 1912, p. 143.

Leucosyrinx kincaidi Dall, Proc. U.S. Nat. Mus. 56, 1920, p. 6.

Solariella kincaidi Tegland, Univ. Cal. Publ. in Geol. Sci. 23 (3), 1933, p. 141.

Spirotrobis vaderensis Weaver and Palmer, var. *kincaidi* Weaver and Palmer, Univ. Wash. Publ. Geol. 1 (3), 1922, p. 36; described in *Turritella.*

Turbonilla (Strioturbonilla) kincaidi Bartsch, Biol. Soc. Wash. 34, 1921, p. 33.

Turris kincaidi Weaver, Univ. Wash. Publ. Geol. 1 (1), 1916, p. 53.

Isopoda

Cirolana kincaidi Hatch, Univ. Wash. Publ. Biol. 10 (5), 1947, p. 208.

Janiropsis kincaidi Richardson, Harriman Alaska Exp. Crustacea X, 1904, p. 221.

Amphipoda

Caprella kincaidi Holmes, Harriman Alaska Exp. 10, 1910, p. 245.

Decapoda (Crustacea)

Spirontocaris kincaidi Rathbun, Proc. U.S. Nat. Mus. 24, 1902, p. 899.

Collembola

Entomobrya kincaidi Folsom, Proc. Wash. Acad. Sci. 4, 1902, p. 96.

Thysanoptera

Hoplothrips kincaidi Moulton, Bull. Brooklyn Ent. Soc. 24, 1929, p. 241.

Homoptera

Aphalara kincaidia Ashmead, Harriman Alaska Exp. Ins. 1, 1904, p. 136.

Megalodontoidea

Acantholyda kincaidi (Rohwer), Can. Ent. 42, 1910, p. 91; described in *Itycorsia* Know.

Monophadnoides kincaidi McGillivray, Univ. Ill. Bul. 20 (50), 1923, p. 26; a synonym of *geniculatus* (Hartig).

Tenthridinoidea

Euura kincaidi (Marlatt), U.S. Dept. of Agr. Div. Ent. Tech. Ser. 3, 1896, p. 33; described in *Pontania*.

Kincaidia n. gen. MacGillivray, Can. Ent. 1914, p. 137; now in *Aglaostigma*.

Monostegis kincaidii MacGillivray, Can. Ent. 25, 1893, p. 239; a synonym of *Empria ignota* Norton.

Ichneumonoidea

Atractodes kincaidi (Ashmead), Proc. Wash. Acad. Sci. 4, 1902, p. 167; described in *Exolytus*.

Colpomera kincaidii (Ashmead), Ins. Life 6, 1904, p. 260; described in *Zaylyptus*.

Cratichneumon kincaidi (Ashmead), Proc. Wash. Acad. Sci. 4, 1902, p. 152; described in *Ichneumon.*

Mesochorus kincaidi Ashmead, Proc. Wash. Acad. Sci. 4, 1902, p. 238.

Olesicampe kincaidi (Davis), Tr. Am. Ent. Soc. 24, 1898, p. 363; described in *Omoborus.*

Stenomachus kincaidi (Ashmead), Proc. Wash. Acad. Sci. 4, 1902, p. 229; described in *Deleter*

Chalcidoidea

Aphycus kincaidi (Timberlake), Pan-Pac. Ent. 6, 1929, p. 43; described in *Metaphycus.*

Cynipoidea

Diastrophus kincaidii Gillette, Can. Ent. 25, 1893, p. 110.

Formicoidea

Leptothorax canadensis Prov. var. *kincaidi* Pergande, Proc. Wash. Acad. Sci. 2, 1900, p. 520; described as a variety of *yankee* Pergande.

Apoidea

Andrena kincaidii Cockerell, Proc. Acad. Nat. Sci. Phila. 1897, p. 351.

Andrena trevoris Cockerell, Entomologist 30, 1897, p. 306.

Bombus kincaidii Cockerell, Ann. Mag. Nat. Hist. (7) 11, 1898, p. 324.

Coelioxys ribis Cockerell var. *kincaidii* Cockerell, Ann. Mag. Nat. Hist. 7 (13), 1904, p. 54.

Colletes kincaidii Cockerell, Bull. Am. Mus. Nat. Hist. 50, 1906, p. 52.

Lasioglossum kincaidii (Cockerell), Can. Ent. 30, 1898, p. 51; described in *Halictus.*

Nomada cressoni trevoriana Cockerell, Can. Ent. 37, 1905, p. 285.

Nomada kincaidiana Cockerell, Proc. Acad. Nat. Sci. Phila. 55, 1903, p. 614.

Osmia kincaidii Cockerell, Proc. Acad. Nat. Sci. Phila. 49, 1897, p. 334.

Osmia trevoris Cockerell, Proc. Acad. Nat. Sci. Phila. 49, 1897, p. 341; *subtrevoris* Cockerell, Bull. Am. Mus. Nat. Hist. 22, 1906, p. 451.

Coleoptera

Agathidium kincaidi Hatch, Jr. N.Y. Ent. Soc. 44, 1936; a synonym of *rotundicollis* Mann.

Amara kincaidi Minsk and Hatch, Bull. Brooklyn Ent. Soc. 34, 1939, p. 217; a synonym of *pallipes* Kby.

Bembidion kincaidi Hatch, Pan-Pac. Ent. 26, 1950, p. 100; a synonym of *falsum* Blais.

Bledius kincaidi Hatch, Beetles of Pacific Northwest 2, 1957, p. 103.

Euaesthetus kincaidi Hatch, Beetles of Pacific Northwest 2, 1957, p. 240.

Hydroporus kincaidi Hatch, Bull. Brooklyn Ent. Soc. 23, 1928, p. 221; a synonym of *rainieri* Hatch.

Hypocaccus lucidulus LeC. var. *kincaidi* McGrath and Hatch, Univ. Wash. Publ. Biol. 10, 1941, p. 62.

Nebria kincaidi Schwarz, Proc. Wash. Acad. Sci. 2, 1900, p. 173.

Scymnus kincaidi Hatch, Beetles of Pacific Northwest, 2, 1957, p. 240.

Siphonaptera

Monopsyllus ciliatus kincaidi Hubbard, Fleas of Western North America, 1946, p. 232.

Diptera

Agromyza kincaidi Molloch, Ann. Ent. Soc. Am. 6, 1913, p. 258; a synonym of *ambigua* Fallen.

Cartosyrphus kincaidia Shannon, Insecutor Inscitiae Menstruus 10, 1922, p. 142; a synonym of *Cheilosia platycera* Hine.

Chrysopilus kincaidi Hardy, Am. Midl. Nat. 41, 1949, p. 156.

Criorhina kincaidi Coquillett, Proc. U.S. Nat. Mus. 23, 1901, p. 611.

Hadroneura kincaidi (Coquillett), Proc. Wash. Acad. Sci. 2, 1900, p. 391; described in *Neoempheria.*

Hoplodictya kincaidi (Johnson), Ann. Ent. Soc. Am. 6, 1913, p. 449; described in *Tetanocera.*

Pericoma kincaidi Quate, Univ. Cal. Publ. Ent. 10, 1955, p. 141.

Pogonota kincaidi Coquillett, Proc. Wash. Acad. Sci. 2, 1900, p. 455; a synonym of *Okeniella dasyprocta* (Loew).

Pyritis kincaidii (Coquillett), Ent. News 6, 1895, p. 131; described in *Volucella.*

Sphenomyia kincaidi Aldrich, Proc. Ent. Soc. Wash. 21, 1919, p. 108; a synonym of *Spilogona leucogaster* Zetterstedt.

Symphoromyia kincaidi Aldrich, Wash. Univ. [St. Louis] Studies 2 (1), 1915, p. 129.

Tipula kincaidi Alexander, Am. Midl. Nat. 42, 1949, p. 278.

Trichoptera

Limnephilus kincaidi Banks, Proc. Wash. Acad. Sci. 3, 1901, p. 468.

Lepidoptera

Phoxopteris kincaidiana Fernald, in Dyar, Proc. Wash. Acad. Sci. 2, 1900, p. 500.

Araneida

Oedothorax kincaidi (Banks), Proc. Ent. Soc. Wash. 7, 1905, p. 96; described in *Gongylidium.*

Elasmobranchii

Raja kincaidi Garman, Bull. Mus. Comp. Zool. 51 (9), 1908, p. 254.

Pisces

Hippocampus kincaidi Townsend and Barbour, Bull. N.Y. Zool. Soc. No. 23, 1906, pp. 304–305.

Malacocottus kincaidi Gilbert and Thompson, Proc. U.S. Nat. Mus. 28, 1905, p. 979.

Publications of Trevor Kincaid

The Psychodidae of Washington. Ent. News, 8, 1897, pp. 143–146.

A new species of *Polyxenus.* Proc. Acad. Nat. Sci. Phila. 9, 1898, pp. 192–193.

The Psychodidae of the Pacific Coast. Proc. Acad. Nat. Sci. Phila. 10, 1899.

Notes on the species of *Crabro* found in the state of Washington. Ent. News 1900, pp. 353–359.

Papers from the Harriman Alaska Expedition, VII. Entomological Results (1): The Tenthredinoidea. Proc. Wash. Acad. Sci. 2, 1900, pp. 341–365. (Harriman Alas. Exp. Ins. 1, 1904, pp. 187–210, pl. xiii–xvii).

Papers from the Harriman Alaska Expedition, XIV. Entomological Results (8): The Sphegoidea and Vespoidea. l.c., pp. 507–510. (Harriman Alaska Exp. Inc. 2, 1904, pp. 107–112).

Notes on American Psychodidae. Ent. News, 1901, pp. 193–195, Fig. 1–9.

The Harriman Alaska Expedition. Mazama 2, 1901, pp. 70–74.

The insects of Alaska. Harriman Alaska Exp. Ins. 2, 1904, pp. 1–34.

Nature study; galls. Bull. Univ. Wash. 4 (3), 1903, pp. 3–15, Fig. 1–27.

Report of gypsy moth work in Russia. pp. 78–83 of Howard and Fiske. The importation into the United States of the parasites of the gypsy moth and the brown-tail moth. U.S. Dept. Agric. Bur. Ent. Bull. 91, 1911, 312 pp.

A proposed school of fisheries. Trans. 2nd Ann. Meeting Pac. Fish. Soc. 1914, pp. 1–6.

Oyster culture in Washington. Trans. 2nd Ann. Meeting Pac. Fish. Soc. 1915, pp. 1–7.

The oyster industry of the Pacific Coast. Pacific Fisherman Yearbook 1916, pp. 67–70, illus.

(and E. Victor Smith) A report on the taking of immature salmon in the coast waters of the state of Washington. 28th and 29th Ann. Rep. St. Fish Comm. to the Gov. of the state of Washington. (1919) 1920, pp. 39–46, (reviewed in Pac. Fisherman 16 (6), June 1918, p. 32 and (9), Sept. 1918, pp. 21, 54, 57).

The edible clams of Puget Sound, *Ibid.*, pp. 47–50, 2 pl.

The oyster reserves of Hoods Canal, *Ibid.*, pp. 51–54, 2 pl.

An annotated list of Puget Sound fishes. 30th and 31st Ann Rep. State Fish Comm. to the Gov. of the state of Washington. 1921, pp. 106–150, 114 fig.

Development of oyster industry of the Pacific. Trans. Am. Fisheries Soc. 58, 1929, pp. 117–122.

The biology of the plankton. The Eleusis of Chi Omega 37 (1), 1935, pp. 37–43.

A half century of biological science. Ore. St. Coll. Seventh Ann. Biol. Colloquium, 1946, pp. 16–19.

Oyster culture. Pac. Northwest Industry 10, 1951, pp. 196–198.

A contribution to the taxonomy and distribution of the American fresh-water Calanoid Crustacea. The Calliostoma Co., Seattle, 1953, 73 pp., 5 pl.

The ant plant, *Orthocarpus pusillus* Bentham; a seemingly new chapter in the ecological relationship between ants and plants. The Calliostoma Co., Seattle, 1954, 12 pp., 6 pl.

Notes and descriptions of American fresh-water Calanoid Crustacea. The Calliostoma Co., Seattle, 1956, 38 pp., 10 pl.

Local races and clines in the marine Gastropod *Thais lamellosa* Gmelin, a population study. The Calliostoma Co., Seattle, 1957, 75 pp., 65 pl.

(with Melville H. Hatch) A list of Coleoptera from the vicinity of Willapa Bay, Washington. The Calliostoma Co., Seattle, 1958, 21 pp., map.

The Staphylinid genera *Pontomalota* and *Thinusa*. The Calliostoma Co., Seattle, 1961, 10 pp., 4 pl.

The ecology and morphology of *Thinobius frizzelli* Hatch, an intertidal beetle. The Calliostoma Co., Seattle, 1961, 15 pp.; 6 pl.

The ant plant, *Orthocarpus pusillus* Bentham. *Trans. Amer. Micro. Soc.* 82, 1963, pp. 101–105, 5 fig.

A Gastropod parasitic on the Holothurian, *Parastichopus californicus* (Stimpson), Trans. Am. Micro. Soc. 83, 1964, pp. 373–376, 7 fig.

Notes on *Thais* (*Nucella*) *lima* (Gmelin), a marine Gastropod inhabiting areas in the North Pacific Ocean. The Calliostoma Co., Seattle, 1964, 41 pp., 18 pl.

The ecology of Willapa Bay, Washington, in relation to the oyster industry. Seattle, 1968, 84 pp. plates (text reproduced photographically).

Bibliography

Published Sources

Anonymous. Preface by Henry Schmitz. 1958. The vision on the knoll. 1861–1961. The first hundred years of the University of Washington. The University of Washington, 31 pp.

Crumb, Samuel Ebb, P. M. Eide, and A. E. Bonn. 1941. The European earwig, *Forticula auricularia* L. U. S. Dept. Agri. Res. Bull. No. 766, 76 p.

Gates, Charles. 1961. The first hundred years of the University of Washington. Univ. Wash. Press. ix + 252 pp.

Hatch, Melville H. (editor). 1950. Studies honoring Trevor Kincaid. Univ. Wash. Press. iii + 140 pp., 12 plates. Contains papers on Trevor Kincaid, Orson Bennett Johnson, and The Young Naturalists' Society by Melville H. Hatch, and 7 research papers by former students and colleagues of Trevor Kincaid.

Howard, Grace E. 1963. Theodore Christian Frye. The Bryologist 66 (3), p. 124–136.

Steele, Earl N. 1964. The immigrant oyster (*Ostrea gigas*) now known as the Pacific oyster. Warren' Quick Print, Olympia, Wash., xiii + 179 pp.

Turner, Neely. 1963. The gypsy moth problem. Conn. Agri. Exp. Sta. Bull. 655, 36 pp.

Unpublished Manuscripts

Condon, Herbert T. 1936. History of the Friday Harbor Station. 6 pp.

Condon, Herbert T., Lyman Phifer, and Rex J. Robinson.

1936. A history of the Oceanographic Laboratories of the University of Washington. 46 pp.

Flahaut, Martha Reekie. 1936. History of the Washington State Museum. 49 pp.

Hatch, Melville H. (editor and compiler). 1936, 1938. History of Zoology at the University of Washington. 147 pp.

Kincaid, Trevor. 1962. Autobiography, the adventures of an omnologist. Revised. 297 pp.

Index